PHILOSOPHY AND HEALTH CARE

Philosophy and Health Care

Edited by

ERIC MATTHEWS
MICHAEL MENLOWE

Avebury
Aldershot · Brookfield USA · Hong Kong · Singapore · Sydney

Published by
Avebury
Ashgate Publishing Limited
Gower House
Croft Road
Aldershot
Hants GU11 3HR
England

Ashgate Publishing Company
Old Post Road
Brookfield
Vermont 05036
USA

A CIP catalogue record for this book is available from the British Library and the US Library of Congress.

ISBN 1 85628 325 9

Printed and Bound in Great Britain by
Athenaeum Press Ltd., Newcastle upon Tyne.

Contents

Notes on contributors

Baruch Brody is Leon Jaworski Professor of Biomedical Ethics and Director of the Centre for Ethics, Medicine and Public Issues at Baylor College of Medicine, Houston, Texas.

A.G.M. Campbell has just retired as Professor of Child Health in the University of Aberdeen, Scotland and as an Honorary Consultant Pediatrician for Grampian Health Board, Scotland.

Grant Gillett is currently Senior Lecturer in Medical Ethics in the Bioethics Research Centre of the University of Otago Medical School, Dunedin, New Zealand.

Matti Hayry is Junior Research Fellow in Practical Philosophy at the University of Helsinki, Finland.

Jennifer Jackson is a Lecturer in Philosophy and Director of the Centre for Business and Professional Ethics at the University of Leeds, England.

David Lamb is a Senior Lecturer in Philosophy at the University of Manchester, England. He is the Editor of Exploration in Knowledge, a journal in the philosophy of science.

Eric Matthews is a Senior Lecturer in the Department of Philosophy, University of Aberdeen, Scotland. He is an Associate Director of Aberdeen's Centre for Philosophy, Technology and Society.

Michael Menlowe is a Lecturer in the Department of Philosophy, University of Edinburgh, Scotland.

Paul T. Menzel is a Professor in the Department of Philosophy, Pacific Lutheran University, Tacoma, Washington State.

Frances Miller is Professor of Law at Boston University School of Law and Professor of Public Health at Boston University School of Medicine.

S.G. Potts is currently a Research Fellow and Honorary Senior Registrar in the University Department of Psychiatry at the Royal Edinburgh Hospital, Scotland.

Peter Singer has been Professor of Philosophy at Monash University, Australia, since 1977 and since 1983 also Director of the Monash University Centre for Human Bioethics. He is a co-editor of the journal Bioethics.

Christopher Tindall is Associate Professor of Philosophy at Trent University, Ontario, Canada.

1 Editors' introduction

Eric Matthews and Michael Menlowe

This volume collects papers confronting a number of controversial and inter-related issues in health care and its economic foundations. The contributors are philosophers, doctors and a lawyer from seven different countries. All except one of the papers were originally delivered at an international conference on medical ethics at the University of Aberdeen, Scotland, in 1989, but they have in most cases been substantially `revised for the present volume.

Allocating Health Care Resources

Baruch Brody offers a distinctive approach to the problem of the allocation of health care resources. Brody asks, given a particular level of wealth, what types of health care should a just society provide for its citizens regardless of ability to pay, while still allowing for the pursuit of other social and individual goals? He argues that expensive technology and an aging population make rationing inevitable. Two forms of rationing ought to be considered: limiting the total amount of money available, leaving it to individual providers to decide how to distribute it; and a central government decision not to provide certain kinds of care for certain patients. Brody raises two objections to both forms of rationing. First, there is no rational basis for decisions. Secondly, both forms involve deceit. He prefers rationing based on the decisions of individual patients. One solution would be to encourage patients to refuse expensive treatments in certain cases. A more comprehensive solution would be to provide individuals with vouchers which they could use to buy private health insurance of the kind they desire. The total expenditure on vouchers would equal the total amount a society is prepared to allocate to the health care of those who cannot buy it. Neither solution directly answers the question, what types of health care should be provided irrespective of ability to pay? Both solutions make the answer a matter of individual, rather than social, choice.

Like Brody, Eric Matthews considers which form of rationing is just. He rejects rationing by the market, since it conflicts with notions of social justice. Rationing by lottery is also unacceptable (see Potts' contribution). While a lottery does achieve a kind of equality, it is an equality based on the exclusion of relevant differences. Matthews argues that a just allocation of health care must include relevant differences. Since the cost of modern health care must be paid for by some collective, Matthews believes that a just distribution of health care should be based on the aims of the collective. He acknowledges that, in any pluralist society, there is the chance that there will be fundamental disagreements about aims. Matthews appeals rather for a general public debate.

Matthews rejects reasoning with QALYs (Quality Adjusted Life Years) as providing solutions to health care allocation problems. S.G. Potts agrees, but he begins his contribution by explaining the attractiveness of the QALY to those who have to make health resource allocation decisions. Cost-benefit analysis does not work, since benefits cannot be expressed in non-financial terms. Cost-effectiveness analysis requires a common non-financial currency, such as the QALY. Dividing QALYs by the cost of the treatment in question yields a measure for cost-effectiveness of treatments. Potts raises two different kinds of objections to allocating resources on the basis of QALYs. First, he objects to cost-effectiveness calculations. Which costs are to be included? The only acceptable answer - all the costs of treatment and non-treatment and all costs borne by tax-funded agencies - makes the calculation complex. Secondly, he objects to the use of the QALY. Why should quality of life be measured only in terms of distress and disability? Whose assessment of the quality of life should be sought? (See Menzel's contribution). Isn't QALY reasoning inherently discriminatory against the old and potentially discriminatory against others on grounds of race and gender? QALY reasoning ignores distributive justice and favours euthanasia, he argues. His own preference is for resource allocation to be based on a lottery (see Matthews' contribution).

As Potts explains, QALY reasoning depends on establishing quality of life indices. Paul Menzel focuses on a number of problems in setting up these indices (some of which have been raised by Potts), and concludes that the use of such indices may be morally justified. The practice of making allocation decisions by adjusting for quality of life may be defended on the grounds of consent. That is, the people most likely to be affected by rationing decisions rank their own lives in terms of quality. But Menzel contends that such ranking could imply consent to rationing decisions only when certain kinds of questions are used to create the rankings. The only questions that ground consent are what Menzel calls 'QALY-bargain questions'. QALY-bargain questions require the respondent to endorse QALYs as an allocation device which exposes him or her to greater risk of dying in return for better quality of life enhancement. Another problem in establishing the indices is deciding who should be questioned. What sample would justify concluding that any individual has consented to QALY-based allocation? If one decides to question only those with experience of impairment in order to avoid bias then, as Menzel illustrates, there are dangers. Respondents may be implicitly rejecting quality-of-life-adjustment reasoning or may be giving responses that cannot be expressed on a single quality of life scale. The danger Menzel warns against is rejecting the preferences rather than the scale.

Embryo experimentation

The moral status of the embryo is a crucial question for those concerned with in vitro fertilisation and certain medical experiments. Whereas the potential benefits of procedures using early embryos is considerable, the objection to using them is that these procedures may involve impermissibly intending the death of human beings. Peter Singer argues that this objection is based on an equivocation. Only persons have a right to life; whereas early embryos are homo sapiens, they are not persons. Nor can an objection to embryo experimentation be made on the grounds that embryos are potential persons. Singer argues that the argument from potential, originally developed in the context of the abortion debate (see Hayry's contribution), has no force in the context of embryo experimentation. Singer's view is that the moral status of the embryo should depend on sentience, and he suggests that experimentation ought to be permissible on embryos up to twenty-eight days old. His view entails that many forms of experimentation on some non-human animal embryos is morally unjustifiable.

Abortion

Matti Hayry considers a potential dilemma for liberal abortion policies: if liberal abortion policies are morally justified, then is not infanticide also justified? Hayry begins by criticizing the standard conservative argument that abortions are wrong because fetuses have a right to life. The premiss that fetuses have a right to life needs justification. Hayry agrees with Singer that the justification that fetuses are potential persons fails. Thus the dilemma arises for proponents of liberal abortion policies: if abortion is justified on the grounds that fetuses are not persons and potential persons have no right to life, then infanticide must be permissible, since infants are not persons.

Hayry considers a number of attempts to distinguish abortion and infanticide. The most apparently successful approach is to argue that birth is a morally-relevant factor. But Hayry does not accept the argument that the difference in our attitude to fetuses and infants is the crucial factor. Rather, the crucial factor is the autonomy of the individual woman. This point needs careful elaboration. If all adults have rights to autonomous action, then to deny females autonomy with respect to their unborn fetuses is nothing less than sexist oppression.

Forbidding infanticide does not unfairly limit one group's autonomy; forbidding abortion does.

Like Hayry, Frances Miller is concerned with a woman's control over decisions affecting both herself and the fetus she carries. Whereas Hayry takes us to the heart of the moral issues about abortion, Miller has a different concern. As a lawyer, she is interested in conflict resolution. She attempts to construct a legal framework for restricting cases in which courts might order, over the mother's objections, treatment of the mother designed to promote the fetus' interests. The legal principle that underlies the framework is that every (competent) person has a right to refuse medical treatment. In Anglo-American jurisprudence, that right is a strong right. The framework is designed to limit fetal-maternal conflict to those cases in which the mother's right to refuse medical treatment could be overcome. The framework consists of a series of six stages, each of which tests whether the presumption in favour of the mother's autonomy is rebutted by the fetus' interests. Only if the proposed treatment satisfies all of the conditions proposed should a court consider ordering the mother to undergo the treatment.

Neonates and Neomorts

There is a considerable need for infant organs, and anencephalic infants are a potential source for such organs. David Lamb considers a number of policy options with regard to the practice of keeping anencephalic infants on respirators in order to remove their organs for transplantation. He rejects the option of re-defining brain death in terms of higher brain functions, since this makes the determination of death depend on the needs of others. He rejects the approach of making anencephaly a special moral or legal category because this leads down a slippery slope. He concludes that maintaining cardio-respiratory functions until brain stem death is an acceptable policy since it is merely delaying an eventual death and does not require any juggling with our accepted definitions of death. As Lamb points out, the issue of using anencephalics for organ harvesting illustrates in a very dramatic way the conflict between the principle of individual care and consideration of the needs of others.

Christopher Tindall expands the issue raised by Lamb. Should we permit the practice of maintaining the respiration and cardiac functions of brain-dead cadavers generally so that we can transplant their organs, use them as blood banks or as subjects for medical experiments? Widespread repugnance is felt at the use of brain-dead cadavers as 'bioemporia' (The expression is Willard Gaylin's. 'Harvesting the Dead', Harper's Magazine, 1974, September 23-46). Tindall considers, and rejects, a number of attempts to show that this repugnance has a sound moral justification. There is, on his view, nothing intrinsically wrong with using brain-dead cadavers as bioemporia. He thinks that the basis of the repugnance lies in our fear of what unrestrained science might do to us. Such a fear must be openly confronted so that society can obtain the considerable benefits of the use of brain-dead cadavers.

Medical technology has recently made it possible to keep alive infants who, but a few years ago, would have had no prospect of life. Alexander Campbell asks when it is permissible not to make use of this technology. First he considers the medical criteria for selective non-treatment of neonates. He concludes that, in cases of infants on the border of viability and those with significant brain abnormality or disease, non-treatment may be justified on medical grounds. As to the ethical considerations, Campbell does not agree with the view that a decision can be based on the infant's interests determined on purely medical grounds. Other factors, loosely and misleadingly called 'quality of life', must be taken into account in determining the infant's best interest. Who should make the decisions? Ideally, it should be the parents and their advisors, together with the relevant medical professionals. When the parents are incapable of making an informed and unbiased decision, then, Campbell claims, the decision must be made by the doctor. Ethical committees may have a useful advisory role, but he fears that their decisions may reflect more concern with the interests of the hospital than with the patient.

Jennifer Jackson considers a familiar distinction which is central to Campbell's argument, as well as to many other aspects of medical practice. It is the distinction often described as the distinction between killing a patient and allowing the patient to die. Jackson claims that the medical consensus supports the view that, while it is always wrong to kill a patient intentionally, it is sometimes permissible to allow a patient to die. The consensus view has been objected to on the grounds that it is unintelligible or inhumane. Jackson argues that it is neither.

The consensus view should be based on the following claim: it is always impermissible to intend an innocent person's death either as a means or an end, but it is sometimes permissible to cause death when death is a foreseen but unintended consequence. So, it would be permissible to allow a patient to die, even by withholding treatment, if, for example, the treatment were not beneficial overall to the patient. Equally, given a correct understanding of what intentional action includes, switching off a respirator may be permissible. The claim that Jackson defends prohibits only treatment which aims at killing the patient. This claim should not be based on a doctrine about the sanctity of life. Rather it should be defended on the grounds that a rule prohibiting killing is socially necessary.

Psychiatry

Grant Gillett uses the poignant case of the New Zealand author Janet Frame to illustrate the conflict between objective and reactive attitudes in psychiatry. Reactive attitudes are those based on our reactions to the intentions we discern in others. Its essence is reciprocity. Objective attitudes are detached, regarding another person as a thing. Psychiatry requires both of these conflicting attitudes. Gillett argues that there is a close connection between our sense of ourselves as persons and reactive attitudes. A person evaluates his or her propositional attitudes (e.g. I want ...; I desire ...) on the basis of norms about, for example, what it is right to want. These norms are derived from reactive attitudes. Thus, reactive attitudes are central to the treatment of mental disorders, the goal of which is to enable the patient to function as a person. But these important reactive attitudes are threatened by the psychiatrist's objective attitudes, and once the objective mode has taken hold of the treatment, it is hard to stop. Gillett contends that objective attitudes must be regarded as provisional and temporary. Psychiatry must aim to understand the interdependence of biology, cognition and interpersonal activity.

2 Ethical reflections on international health care expenditures

Baruch Brody

One way of comparing systems of health care is to contrast modes of delivery and sources of funds. At one extreme are countries where all health care facilities are owned by the government, all health care personnel work for the government, and the entire system is funded by taxes. Great Britain used to come close to that, but it now has a growing private sector. At the other extreme are countries where all facilities are privately owned, all health care personnel work for those facilities or are self-employed, and all health care is paid for by the recipients, perhaps with the aid of private health insurance. Some capitalist-oriented third world countries come close to that. In between are systems of private ownership of facilities with publicly financed universal insurance (Canada comes close to that) and very mixed systems (the U.S., with public as well as private facilities, public as well as private insurance schemes, and gaps in between).

This paper will not in any way address the issue of the merits and demerits of each of these approaches. My reason for this is straightforward: I believe that with the exception of societies employing extreme systems, most goals for health care systems can be obtained by societies employing any of these approaches. I am concerned instead with the goals of health care systems. In particular, I am concerned with what I take to be the central goals-question of health policy throughout the world today: What types of health care should a just society provide to all of its citizens, regardless of their ability to pay for it, while still allowing for the social pursuit of other goals and the individual pursuit of private goals? Note that I am presupposing that citizens are free to purchase additional health care as part of that pursuit of their private goals.

My strategy in this paper will be as follows: In the opening section, I will review certain facts about health care expenditures in the developed world. I will then offer a reformulation of our question suggested by those facts. In the second section, I will discuss an attempt to avoid dealing with our reformulated question. In the third section, I will suggest that our question is usually resolved in ways that have unacceptable implications. In the fourth section, I will argue for an entirely different approach both to the question and to its resolution.

I. Facts and reformulations

The data we will be examining come from the OECD (Organization for Economic Cooperation and Development), which is to be thanked for making it possible for the first time for scholars to begin a serious study of international health care expenditures and their implications for the goals of public health policy. It is true that Reidar Lie and I have recently shown[1] that there are fundamental conceptual problems raised by the OECD conceptualization of many issues, but none of this affects the validity of the data I will use in this paper.

I want to begin with an exhibit which clearly indicates the fundamental trend in health care expenditures throughout the world since 1960. The fundamental trend revealed in the exhibit is straightforward: all of the developed countries have seen a substantial growth in the percentage of their GDP devoted to health care in the last twenty-five years. From this theme many have drawn the conclusion that our different societies face a crisis as they confront the ever increasing percentage of GDP devoted to health care. Naturally, such a conclusion needs considerable justification. One might equally conclude from the data that the different countries are now finally providing to more of their citizens more of the health care to which they are entitled. Obviously, the factual data by themselves don't settle these issues; we will return to them below. The exhibit is as follows:[2]

Exhibit 1.1
Total health expenditures as a percentage of Gross Domestic Product, 1970-1989

	1970	1975	1980	1985	1986	1987	1988	1989
Australia	4.9%	5.5%	6.5%	7.0%	7.1%	7.1%	6.9%	7.0%
Austria	5.4	7.3	7.9	7.6	8.3	8.4	8.3	8.2
Belgium	4.1	5.9	6.3	6.9	7.2	7.3	7.3	7.2
Canada	7.1	7.2	7.4	8.5	8.8	8.8	8.6	8.7
Denmark	6.1	6.5	6.8	6.3	6.0	6.3	6.4	6.3
Finland	5.7	6.3	6.5	7.2	7.4	7.4	7.2	7.1
France	5.8	7.0	7.6	8.5	8.5	8.5	8.6	8.7
Germany	5.9	8.2	8.5	8.6	8.5	8.6	8.9	8.2
Greece	4.0	4.1	4.3	4.9	5.4	5.2	5.1	5.1
Iceland	5.2	6.2	6.5	7.4	7.8	7.9	8.5	8.6
Ireland	5.6	7.6	9.0	8.3	8.3	8.0	7.9	7.3
Italy	5.2	6.1	6.8	7.0	6.9	7.3	7.6	7.6
Japan	4.4	5.5	6.4	6.5	6.7	6.8	6.7	6.7
Luxembourg	4.1	5.6	6.8	6.8	6.7	7.2	7.3	7.4
Netherlands	6.0	7.7	8.2	8.2	8.1	8.5	8.4	8.3
New Zealand	5.2	6.7	7.2	6.6	6.9	7.3	7.4	7.1
Norway	5.0	6.7	6.6	6.4	7.1	7.5	7.4	7.6
Portugal	–	6.4	5.9	7.0	6.6	6.4	6.5	6.3
Spain	3.7	4.8	5.6	5.7	5.6	5.7	6.0	6.3
Sweden	7.2	7.9	9.5	9.3	9.0	9.0	9.0	8.8
Switzerland	5.2	7.0	7.3	7.6	7.6	7.9	8.0	7.8
Turkey	–	3.5	4.1	–	–	3.5	–	–
United Kingdom	4.5	5.5	5.8	6.0	6.0	5.9	5.9	5.8
United States	7.4	8.4	9.3	10.6	10.8	11.1	11.3	11.8
Mean*	5.4	6.5	7.1	7.4	7.6	7.6	7.6	

Source: **Health OECD, Facts and Trends** (Paris: OECD, forthcoming).
*Mean excluding Turkey.

A second important theme which emerges from this exhibit is that different countries spend very different percentages of their GDP on health care, ranging from Greece (5.1% in 1989) to the United States (11.8% in 1989). Of particular interest, however, is that the source of health care expenditures is not all that significant in determining the percentage. The two countries which spend the highest percentage of their GDP on health care are the U.S. and Sweden, and the U.S. percentage of public expenditures for health care is the lowest while the Swedish percentage is among the highest. You get much more insight into what determines the level of health care expenditures when you look at per capita spending on health care compared to per capita GDP. The following exhibit demonstrates this point: [Table 1.2 on p.13].[3]

The more affluent a country is (expressed in per capita GDP), the more it spends on health care per person. It turns out that 77% of the variation in health care spending is due just to this matter of different wealth.

To my mind, this perspective suggests that the whole question of what is the right amount or the right percentage of the GDP to spend on what types of health care is ill-framed. As a country gets wealthier, it has the capacity to spend a higher percentage of its GDP on things other than basic needs, and more expensive forms of health care begin to seem more and more appropriate. I would therefore like to suggest that we reformulate our question as follows: given a particular level of wealth, what types of health care should a just society provide to all of its citizens, regardless of their ability to pay for it, while still allowing for the social pursuit of other goals and the individual pursuit of private goals? The data we have presented are not of course proof that the question should be reformulated this way, but they suggest this as a reasonable reformulation.

This point can also be put as follows: One quick answer to the question of what types of health care a society is required to provide to all of its citizens, regardless of their ability to pay for it, is that any society is obliged to provide all of the health care from which its citizens could benefit. After all, health care is a basic need, so why isn't everyone entitled to receive all of that basic need from which they can benefit? There is, however, a

Exhibit 1.2
Health and wealth in OECD countries, 1987

Per capita health expenses ($PPP)

2,500
2,000
1,500
1,000
500
0

1.	Australia	7.	France	13.	Japan	19.	Spain
2.	Austria	8.	Germany	14.	Luxembourg	20.	Sweden
3.	Belgium	9.	Greece	15.	Netherlands	21.	Switzerland
4.	Canada	10.	Iceland	16.	New Zealand	22.	Turkey
5.	Denmark	11.	Ireland	17.	Norway	23.	United Kingdom
6.	Finland	12.	Italy	18.	Portugal	24.	United States

0 2 4 6 8 10 12 14 16 18

Source: Exhibit 3 and **National Accounts, Main Aggregates**, vol. 1 (Paris: OECD, 1989).
Note: PPP = purchasing power parity. PCH = per capita health spending. PCGDP = per capita gross domestic product. PCH = − 363 + 0.105 x PCGDP. Both the constant term and the regression coefficient are statistically significant at the 0.1 level. R^2 = .86 (adjusted correlation coefficient squared).

good reason to reject that answer. The claim that everyone should receive all of the health care from which they will benefit is simply insensitive to the fact that someone else must pay for the health care, and pays no attention to the question whether those others really have the obligation to fund that much health care. Those who insist that we have an obligation to provide all of the health care from which people could benefit regardless of their ability to pay for it simply fail to consider how the obligation to provide health care (and the correlative right to the health care) fits into a network of other rights, obligations, and values. What our data suggest, however, is that the social obligation to provide health care may grow as the country's wealth grows just because providing that additional care doesn't overburden - in a more affluent country - the rest of the network of rights, obligations, and values. But, of course, this is just a suggestion. An argument for it would require an entire theory of distributive justice, one which argues that social obligations are determined more by social wealth than by recipient need. I have presented such a theory elsewhere;[4] the most I can do now is to commend this thought to you for further reflection.

II. Mistaken attempts

If we reject the view that we are obliged to provide all the health care from which all citizens can benefit, regardless of their ability to pay, then we will have to engage in rationing. By rationing, I mean the deliberate decision to refuse to provide people health care which they want and from which they could benefit because we refuse to bear the cost.

There are some who hope that we could avoid rationing. Their hope is that eliminating waste and emphasizing preventive medicine will enable countries, at a wide variety of levels of affluence, to provide to all of their citizens all the forms of health care from which they can benefit.[5] I am a great believer both in avoiding waste and in preventive medicine. I believe in the former because I like to spend money on programes that provide benefits. I believe in the latter because it is likely to enable people to live longer and richer lives. But we only fool ourselves - and not for very long - if we believe that eliminating waste and emphasizing preventive medicine will do the job. As has been shown,[6] these measures only produce one-time savings that lower the baseline of expenditures but do not impact upon the rate of growth which is determined by other factors. The factors in question are technological advances and demography. Let me elaborate upon both.

One of these factors is the continued growth of new expensive technologies. Consider the organ transplant programme. Liver transplants and heart transplants have joined kidney transplants as the treatment of choice for certain conditions. These procedures are not wasteful, given their success rates, so mechanisms designed to eliminate waste will not in the long run enable us to avoid the heavy expenses of these transplant programmes. New surgical procedures such as transplantation are not the only forms of new expensive technologies; medications provide us with another but not the only example. Consider AZT for sufferers from AIDS and TPA for victims of heart attacks. In short, the first reason why eliminating waste and emphasizing prevention will not be enough is that medical scientists are doing a good job in developing new efficacious techniques, but ones that are very expensive. Being careful not to use them wastefully, and emphasizing prevention to minimize their need, will help, but the drive of technology will surely lead us to tremendous additional costs.

There is a second factor that is extremely relevant here and which is an additional part of the reason why all of these cost control measures will not be enough. This factor is the aging of society. Maximum human life span has not changed significantly, and there is a well known debate as to whether it is likely to change at all.[7] But there is a dramatic increase in average life expectancy that has allowed many more people to survive into old age. All this may be for the good, but it does mean increasing health care costs.[8] Of particular concern is the group over 75 and, to an even greater extent, the group over 85. Members of these very old groups are far more likely to need care for a wide variety of chronic illnesses, and, in many cases, they will also need custodial nursing home care. Nursing home costs are already growing rapidly, and that increase in costs is before the major increase in the percentage of the very elderly in our population. Moreover, all projections for care for chronic illnesses and for custodial care are probably underestimates because they fail to take into account further medical developments that will enable us to expand the life expectancy of even more citizens. In some sense, the potential successes of preventive medicine have extremely frightening implications in this context, for they may mean even more people reaching these very old ages with tremendous demands on the health care system. In short, the second reason why rationing will be needed is the demographic factor of an aging population.

We have here then the crucial arguments that rationing will be needed at most levels of social affluence. Successful medicine, a medicine which combines preventive medicine which lessens the development of life-threatening conditions with advances in high technology medicine which saves lives if those conditions do develop, will result in a level of health care expenditures that continues to rise rapidly no matter how much we eliminate waste. The conclusion is that few if any societies will be obliged to provide all the medical care for all of its citizens from which they can benefit if those societies are to meet other social goals and to enable individuals to meet private goals, and that rationing will be required.

III. Problems with the usual forms of rationing

Two major approaches to rationing types of care are usually adopted. The first involves a national budgetary policy which limits the amount of care which can be provided but leaves the actual decision about which forms of care to provide to individual providers (hospitals and/or physicians). The second involves a governmental decision not to provide certain types of care to certain recipients.

Aaron and Schwartz, in their recent study of rationing of health care in Great Britain,[9] have shown the extent to which the British rely upon the first type of policy. Consider, for example, the fact that the British do not use TPN (total parenteral nutrition) as much as America does. On a population-corrected basis, they spend less than one-fourth as much as the U.S. does. There is no national policy limiting in any way the use of TPN, and since its use involves no special capital facilities or major equipment, its use is not restricted by any national policy restrictions on capital expenditures. Rather, each hospital's pharmacy has a budget, and when the use of TPN rises, the chief pharmacist is able effectively to stop further use of TPN on the grounds that it blocks other care. In one large teaching hospital, Aaron and Schwartz report, pressure from the chief pharmacist led the staff to agree that a maximum of six adult patients could receive TPN at any one time. The relevant consultants then had to decide who would get that form of care and who would not, even if they could benefit from it. Similar patterns emerge in many other British examples of rationing.

This form of rationing is not unique to Great Britain. A very similar phenomenon is emerging in the United States in connection with thrombolytic agents for patients during heart attacks. Two agents are available, Streptokinase ($200) or TPA ($2,200). A recent study[10] showed that patients in some hospitals are getting Streptokinase rather than TPA, although their physicians believe that TPA is better. Again, it is not a matter of national policy. It is just that individual institutions have to work within their budget, and it helps if they use Streptokinase and ration the use of TPA.

The second form of rationing is best illustrated by the recent decision of the state of Oregon to adopt a comprehensive prioritization of health care interventions followed by a rationing policy which will mean that society will not provide certain forms of care to patients even if they could benefit from those forms of care.[11] We do not yet know which of these services will not be provided; it depends on the level of funding set by the legislature. But the crucial point is that this will be centralized rationing rather than individual provider rationing.

I am troubled by both of these forms of rationing. I will present here a revised version of two arguments that I have offered elsewhere,[12] one that there is no rational basis for making such decisions and the other that it inevitably involves deceit. There is actually a third argument which I would offer (that the rationed funds belong to the recipient, and not to us, so they should choose), but it depends upon my already-alluded to theory of justice, so I must leave a full presentation of it to another occasion.

In order to make the first point, let me briefly indicate two recent examples of studies of very routine medical procedures and of their costs and benefits. I have deliberately chosen to stay away from the dramatic examples used above, because I want to remind us that adopting either of the approaches to rationing mentioned above means raising these types of issues for thousands of day-by-day medical procedures. Here are the examples.

The first involves a study of the routine use of chest x-rays upon the admission of patients to a hospital.[13] The authors suggested that spending money on these routine chest x-rays was a wasteful health care expenditure, but their own data suggest that the most they could claim was that the expenditure was too great for the modest benefits obtained. After all, they recognized that there was a small percentage of cases (4%) in which routine chest x-rays picked up a problem which was not known about before and which was treatable upon its discovery. So each patient who received the routine chest x-ray did receive the statistical benefit of improving their chance of getting health care for all their problems, including ones unknown upon admission. Among those problems was an unknown potentially curable lung-cancer. However, the cost for all the x-rays required to find these treatable problems was very high, and the authors recommended not spending the money for that purpose. Is that a reasonable conclusion? Do the benefits in question justify those expenditures? Or should we ration routine chest x-rays? How should we decide?

A second example[14] raises the same issues. Women with a history of genital herpes who become pregnant require screening to ascertain whether they have an active infection close to the time of the birth of their child. If they do, they need to have a caesarean section in order to avoid transmitting genital herpes to their child. There are two ways in which they can be screened. One, which is much less expensive, is simply undergoing a physical examination. Unfortunately, this will not pick up cases of subclinical infections. The second is undergoing weekly viral cultures in the last weeks before delivery. This more expensive approach will pick up additional cases of recurring genital herpes. How much does this cost? A recent study suggests that the cost of each case of neonatal herpes prevented by such screening is $1,840,000. Is this a reasonable health care expenditure? Or should viral cultures be rationed?

These simple examples help us see why a rationing policy of either type is not a viable policy. These forms of rationing require us to compare the costs and benefits of thousands of interventions and decide which are in and which are out in the light of the benefits and costs. The data for doing this are just not available. In the end, Oregon had to give up its attempt to do this, and adopt a much more simplistic approach which does not even address these two examples and others like them.

Note, moreover, that I have used examples where everyone will agree that the results (detecting a potentially treatable lung mass or avoiding neonatal herpes) are beneficial. Things are even worse when you consider possible 'benefits' that only some find beneficial (e.g., abortions and infertility treatments, psychiatric care for problems in living, orthodontic care, growth hormone therapy, cosmetic surgery, etc.). Without an objective theory of the good, how can society as a whole or individual providers decide for a considerable number of potential beneficiaries with differing values whether these are even benefits, much less whether they are sufficiently beneficial so that they should be provided under some rationing scheme? Even if we had data about the outcomes of these forms of therapy, we would still need some basis for deciding whether these outcomes are beneficial, and, if they are, what is the extent of the benefits they provide. Lacking such a theory of the good, we cannot decide what a rational rationing scheme should do about these interventions. It is worth reflecting on what was the rational basis for Oregon's decision to give a far higher prioritization to abortion on demand than to certain forms of infertility treatment. Was it anything more than imposing the values of the majority on everyone else?

I turn now to my second objection, the objection that rationing involves deceit. Let me begin by examining how rationing actually works in the British setting. How does rationing actually work? How do British physicians, for example, manage to avoid dialyzing patients whose life would be saved by dialysis? Let me quote from Aaron and Schwartz's recent study of rationing in the British health care system:[15]

> British physicians are candid about the way they discourage patients from insisting on dialysis. Asked how he would explain to her family the prospects of a 65 year old woman with kidney failure, one general practitioner first told us that he did not think that it was up to him to decide whether she should be dialyzed, that he would leave the decision to the consultant... When pressed on whether he might save everyone time and anguish by discouraging referral, he described how he would talk to the family. "I would say that mother's or aunt's kidneys have failed or are failing and there is little that anyone can do about it because of her age and general physical state, and that it would be my suggestion and my advice that we spare her any further investigation, and further painful procedure, and we would just make her as comfortable as we can for what remains of her life". Remarkably few of the criteria for rejection are explicitly stated. Age, for example, is not officially identified as an obstacle to treatment... Because of the respect that most patients have for physicians, the recommendation of the doctors is usually followed with little complaint, particularly when the disease does not manifest itself in a way that is recognizable to the patient or when it is only one manifestation of a multifaceted disorder like diabetes.

What is wrong with such an approach? It seems obvious that rationing works because the patients are passive and accept, out of respect for the physician's authority, the claim that nothing more can really be done. Moreover, it seems clear that these physicians are at best deceiving their patients and at worst are just lying to them. It is just not true about these elderly patients that 'there is very little that anyone can do about it'. Patients can be kept alive, even if they are elderly and diabetic, for considerable periods of time with careful aggressive management of kidney failure through dialysis and relevant support. So Aaron and Schwartz's study suggests, as we might have suspected anyway, that rationing requires patient passivity and a fair amount of deceit.

There is a response to this argument, offered in a recent article by Norman Daniels,[16] which needs to be considered further. Daniels claims that rationing would not necessarily involve deceit if the issues were discussed publicly in advance of a particular patient being ill so that members of society perceived that the decisions to ration care were fair rational decisions made socially and not prejudicial decisions of individual physicians in particular cases. [See Eric Matthews' paper in this volume (eds)]. But I think that this is unlikely to work for several reasons:

(a) The affluent will, presumably, continue to be able to purchase at extra cost the care otherwise rationed. A public understanding of the situation will include, therefore, a public understanding that some will die or suffer serious harm because they did not receive the care that others who are more affluent did receive. This is a hard message for people to accept, and the difficulty will therefore lead to a desire to keep rationing decisions private rather than public.

(b) It is one thing for society to agree in advance that certain care be rationed. It is another thing to accept the rationing when one or one's family is ill and is having care rationed. The difficulty of obtaining patient and family acceptance *at this point* is what drives providers to deceit or at least to minimize awareness; [See Paul T. Menzel's paper in this volume (eds)].

(c) Daniels overestimates, to my way of thinking, the extent to which people will see the rationing decision as fair just because it was made in some public political process. Given the alienation of so many citizens from the political process, they may just see it as one more way in which they are being mistreated by politicians and powerful interest groups. Physicians who want to avoid confronting this issue will wind up employing deceit.

IV. My solution

How then ought we decide what types of medical care we should provide to those who can benefit from it? In this final section, I would like to briefly present two suggestions which I have developed elsewhere.[17] I believe that both of them deserve careful consideration as alternatives to the approaches we examined in the previous section.

Both of these proposals have one fundamental theme in common. It is their emphasis on the individual rationing choices of patients rather than on collective social rationing choices. Both of these proposals postulate as an essential value the value of individual choice and freedom.

Let us begin with the first proposal. Suppose that all of the following three hypotheses are valid:

> (a) There are several large classes of patients (e.g. persistent vegetative patients, patients with severe and degenerating physical or intellectual impairments, terminally ill patients who are now in multi-organ system failure) about whom there is general (even if not complete) agreement that various levels of aggressive and expensive health care could be withheld and/or withdrawn, providing that the patient, if competent, or the family or guardian, if the patient is incompetent, concurs.
>
> (b) Health care that could be limited with that concurrence is presently often provided, primarily because the question of its provision is not raised by any of the parties involved.
>
> (c) There are substantial costs incurred in the provision of this care and instituting measures to limit it could provide considerable savings in our national health care budget.

If all three of these hypotheses are valid, then we would have a proposal for meeting at least part of the problem of rising health care expenditures which would avoid the objections we raised to social rationing. It would involve patients or families honestly and openly choosing to refuse certain forms of care rather than physicians rationing care in a deceitful manner, and it would have a principled rational basis for not providing care (patient or family refusal) rather than the pretence that care is not being provided as the result of an objective rationing system based on objective assessments of benefits and costs.

Would the withholding of further aggressive medical care in such cases make a significant dent in national health care expenditures? It is impossible at this point to answer that question definitively. But there are reasons for being optimistic. The very factors that are going to cause a crisis, no matter how much we avoid waste (an increasingly aging population which can be kept alive with high technology medicine) are the very factors which are involved in so many of these cases. So many of the patients in these classes are patients who are old and who are kept alive by highly aggressive measures. A policy of agreeing to withhold care at the request of these patients coupled with a policy of always honestly providing that option to the patients might by itself be enough to make a major impact upon rising health care costs. In any case, there is no need to speculate on this question; the data from the forthcoming Phase II of the SUPPORT study[18] will shed considerable light on the contribution such an approach might make to controlling health care costs.

I see the following as the major potential difficulties with this first proposal: (a) health care providers might not be comfortable with providing patients and/or families with the option of receiving palliative care rather than the currently provided aggressive care; (b) health care recipients and/or their families might not be willing to accept the alternative of palliative care even if it were offered; (c) we might not even be able to have a social consensus about the types of cases in which we wish to encourage presenting patients and/or their families with a choice of life-prolonging care vs. palliative care. Hopefully, the data from Phase II of SUPPORT will help us assess the extent to which these potential difficulties can be overcome.

This is the first of my proposals for dealing with the problem of rising health care costs. It is obvious that the theme of patient choice is central to that proposal. And it is, of course, this theme which differentiates my first proposal - and the second to follow - from the above-criticized rationing proposals. This recognition of the centrality of patient choice in my first proposal suggests the possibility of still further ways of dealing with our problem by employing the theme of patient choice.

My next proposal allows more questions to be answered by the recipients and not by society in general. Suppose we have decided that there is a certain amount of money that we are prepared to allocate to health care expenditures for those who cannot pay for health care themselves. The question that is posed for any rationing policy is which health care to provide. My second suggestion is that we don't need to answer that question. We could simply provide that level of funding in the form of a voucher to citizens and allow them to choose among insurance schemes for the provision of health care. They might choose to join some scheme which emphasizes more preventive medicine and extensive testing and which provides that by not funding certain expensive high technology last ditch efforts. Thus, to refer to our earlier examples, they would get routine chest x-rays and viral cultures but not organ transplants. They might choose a more catastrophe oriented policy, one which downplays primary care and preventive medicine. Then they would get the transplants but no routine chest x-rays or viral cultures. Why do we need to make that choice as opposed to their making that choice? Why not develop our system around the theme of liberty?

Notice again that this scheme avoids the major difficulties that we raised against rationing. This is a scheme that involves patient decision-making and patient honest understanding rather than deceit and ignorance. The health care that the patients receive and the health care that they do not receive will be determined on a principled basis, namely, their choices given budget constraints, and not by some rationing decision made by others using the pretence that there are both the outcome data and the objective value scheme required for an objective other-imposed rationing scheme.

Note that this second proposal can incorporate within it the first proposal. One scheme which many might well choose to purchase is one which offers better health care at earlier stages of life by avoiding costs at later stages of life through a policy of aggressively questioning people about the use of life preserving technologies in certain contexts. Many, but by no means all, patients would probably opt for such a scheme. So the adoption of the second approach would, in fact, be a continuation of the first approach.

Naturally, this proposal doesn't answer one crucial question. There remains the background question of what percentage of our GDP should be devoted to providing health care. But neither of the alternative approaches does that. Both British localized rationing and Oregon centralized rationing leave that decision to the political process, either in deciding what budget to provide to institutions (in the British case) or in deciding how far down the list of priorities will be funded (in the case of Oregon). My proposals can do that as well, although they do impose the constraint that the decision should increase in generosity as the wealth of the society in question increases. I actually am working on a broader theory of social justice that will, I hope, shed light on what that percentage ought to be. But that is for another day.

Variations of this second scheme have been offered by a number of authors.[19] Their main interest in it seems to relate to its potential efficiency. Consumers choosing among these plans will have an incentive to choose more efficient providers so that the consumers can get more for their money. I have no objection to that efficiency, but I do want to make it clear that my main reason for advocating such a voucher scheme is that it offers, it seems to me, the only basis for an honest rationing scheme with a rational basis.

I have made two proposals, each of an increasingly broad nature, on how to deal with the question of what forms of health care should be socially funded. Neither of these proposals attempts to answer the question directly. What each does is create decisional processes which enable those who will receive the health care to answer the question. In the first proposal, they would simply be given an option, which they should have anyway, about whether they should receive certain life-preserving care. The second proposal would provide funds to them, allowing them to make choices about their health care in general rather than imposing the choices upon them in a social rationing process.

When I make these proposals, there is an objection that is always raised, the objection of the patient at the hospital door. It runs in its most dramatic

fashion as follows: suppose that one of the recipients of these vouchers makes choices, even reasonable choices, that do not cover insurance for some life-saving therapy for some illness. Suppose now that he or she contracts that illness and arrives uncovered by insurance at the hospital. Would we, and should we, turn them away and allow them to die? And if not, doesn't that mean that the suggestion about patient choice collapses?
I think not, but the answer is complex. At least the following points need to be made:

(a) If we have in place an adequate redistributive programme, and if this patient had the opportunity to make informed choices about the use of funds earlier on, we would be under no obligation of justice to provide that care and he or she would have no right to it;
(b) We might nevertheless do so, either out of a sense of compassion or a sense of respect for human life. Justice is not the only reason for providing health care;
(c) We should not do so if we become convinced that it would contribute to setting an example which led others to neglect appropriate health care expenditures with the expectation that extra social funding for medical emergencies would always be available. Also, we should not do so if it resulted in unfair burdens on others.

Let me conclude with one observation. I have been alluding throughout this paper to my general theory of distributive justice according to which those who receive health care from social funding are actually receiving benefits from funds which belong to them. I have not in this paper been able to explain and argue for this general theory. But if I am right, then there is an even more fundamental argument against social rationing and for my schemes: we have no right to decide for others how money which belongs to them should be spent for their benefit. Only they have a right to do that.

Notes

1. Brody and Lie (forthcoming).
2. Schieber and Poullier (1991), p. 109.

3. Schieber and Poullier (1989), p. 173.
4. Brody (1983).
5. Angell (1985).
6. Schwartz (1987).
7. This debate was, in large measure, provoked by Fries (1980).
8. Extensive data can be found in Office of Technology Assessment (1985).
9. Aaron and Schwartz (1984).
10. Brody *et al.* (1991).
11. The fullest account of the Oregon plan is to be found in the recently issued report obtainable from the Oregon Health Services Commission entitled 'The 1991 Prioritization of Health Services'.
12. See my 'The macro-allocation of health care resources', in Sass and Massey (1988), pp. 213-36.
13. Hubbell *et al.* (1985).
14. Binkin *et al.* (1984).
15. Aaron and Schwartz (1984), pp.36f.
16. Daniels (1986).
17. I first made this proposal in my paper 'The interaction between ethics and economics in planning health care for the aged', in Gaitz *et al.* (1985), pp. 335-40. I have elaborated upon it in the following two publications: 'Wholehearted and halfhearted care', in Spicker *et al.* (1987), pp. 79-94, and Brody 'The macro-allocation of health care resources', *op. cit.*
18. Dawson *et al.* (1990).
19. Most recently in Enthoven and Kronick (1989) and Butler (1991).

3 The ethics of rationing

Eric Matthews

Introduction

The notion of rationing medical care seems to be intrinsically repugnant to many people, not least to many health care professionals. Rationing is rejected as essentially unethical. What I shall try to show is that this rejection is confused: that there is nothing unethical about rationing medical care *in itself*, although some *forms* of rationing may be unacceptable. Indeed, I shall go further and argue that in some situations a certain kind of rationing may be an ethical imperative .

Much of the confusion I refer to arises from a lack of clarity about the concept of rationing itself. To ration something is clearly to distribute or allocate that thing as between different recipients: but not any form of allocation will count as rationing. Allocation on a purely random basis, for example, will not - as when I throw all the chocolates in the air and allow anyone to take away as many as they can happen to catch. In order for a distribution to count as rationing, it must be based on some rational principle or other. Part of the trouble which has arisen in discussions about the rationing of medical care is due to the fact that there can be various kinds of principle, all rational in some respect or other, on which medical resources can be allocated. Identifying rationing with only one of these, which they reject on moral grounds, opponents of rationing consider themselves to have shown that it is intrinsically immoral - that a rational allocation cannot be a moral allocation.

Ethics and resource allocation

Those who follow what might be called the 'Hippocratic' tradition of medical thought, for instance, sometimes regard the very thought of allocation at all as in conflict with a doctor's ethical obligations. In that tradition, the doctor's prime duty is to do all that he or she can for each individual patient: even to consider making choices between patients seems at first sight inconsistent with that duty. But making choices between patients is unavoidable: a doctor's time and energy are themselves finite resources, and a minute devoted to one patient is a minute taken away from another. The doctor must decide whether doing his or her best for an old lady with arthritis, for instance, is more or less of an obligation than doing his or her best for a young woman with migraine. In modern medicine, of course, doctors have other finite resources to consider, apart from their own time and energy - equipment, drugs, nursing care, beds and so on and so forth. And the method by which this very expensive modern health care needs to be funded creates further moral dilemmas: is doing one's best for the old lady consistent with the purposes for which funds were given, whether by taxpayers in the National Health Service or by premium payers in systems of state or private insurance? If allocation decisions are unavoidable, then since 'ought implies can', they cannot be intrinsically immoral. The only remaining question is whether there is any rational and morally acceptable principle on which such decisions can be based, whether they are decisions between one individual patient and other, or choices between whole areas of medical treatment, such as neonatal intensive care and long-stay geriatric hospitals.

The market principle

Some people, particularly in the present climate of opinion, would argue that the only intelligible basis for allocation decisions is the consumer preferences of patients themselves, and so that the only rational principle which can be used is the market principle. Rationing of medical care should be based on price alone. Some might also want to maintain that basing allocation on the market in this way has a moral advantage, in that it respects patient autonomy by allowing patients themselves to make allocation decisions, and in that it does not make invidious moral distinctions between one human being and another. A person's preferences are just a fact about that person: to allocate resources of any kind on the basis of consumer preferences is precisely not to treat one consumer as being more morally deserving than another.

Although the market model may have moral advantages in this sense, however, it is easy to see why it also offends against most people's conception of justice. Many would see considerations of justice as having a particular relevance to the allocation of health care resources, because, as Norman Daniels[1] puts it, 'Health care is special'. We do not regard most forms of medical care as mere commodities, like refrigerators or videos. If I want a video and cannot afford to pay for it, then no injustice is done to me if the shopkeeper refuses to supply me with one: if he took pity on my plight and gave me one, that would be an act of pure charity on his part. But if I need medical treatment and an appropriately qualified and equipped doctor refuses to give it to me simply because I am too poor to pay for it, then it would seem to many (perhaps not to all) that an injustice would be done to me.

The rationality of that view depends, clearly, on a distinction between consumer wants or preferences and human needs, combined with a notion of a *right* to medical care which rests on the existence of a medical need. Baruch Brody[2] has argued that, even if we accept that we do all equally have medical needs, it is an unsupported assumption that such a need generates a right. Questions of justice, for him and others who think like him, do indeed concern human rights: 'one of the fundamental human rights is the right not to be constrained or coerced from so acting [i.e. from acting as one freely chooses] by others'.[3] Judged by this standard, notions of distributive justice which entail that human beings should be constrained by law and regulation to act in certain ways (e.g. to belong to a universal health-care scheme) are in fact profoundly unjust. However, Brody also argues, on social contract grounds, that 'legitimate private property rights presuppose some redistribution of wealth'.[4] The argument is that the right to private property depends, as Locke contended, on the labour by which the property-owner developed a portion of the land which was originally the common property of all. However, the wealth produced by labour in this way depended in its turn on the initial value of the natural resources used, the right to which was denied to other members of the society by the developer's exclusive property-rights. Brody concludes that it would be just to compensate the other members of society for that loss in the form of socially-recognized rights to a minimum level of support.

Expressed in more concrete terms, Brody's argument goes like this:

> ...the natural resources of the earth are leased to those who develop them, or to those to whom they transfer those leases. In return they owe a rental to everyone. That rental is collected as taxes and paid into a social insurance fund which covers everyone equally. The social insurance fund insures us against destitution and it pays payments to those who are destitute.[5]

The application of this model to health care is seen by Brody as taking the form of cash payments to the indigent, rather than provision of services in kind. Individuals would then have the free choice as to how to spend their entitlement, depending on their own view of their medical needs: in this way, the essential libertarian requirement of free individual choice would be preserved.

The contorted nature of Brody's argument to this conclusion is in itself a sign of something wrong. In effect, he acknowledges the relevance of considerations of justice and rights to health care (and other forms of social welfare), but seeks to fit that acknowledgement into a generally libertarian framework. If citizens have a right to a redistribution of social resources in order to provide them with health care, however, then it is hard to see how this differs from a right to health care *tout court*. And if they have such a right, then it cannot be based simply on their *felt* need or preference, but on their *objective* human need for health care. Health care remains 'special'.

The argument so far can be summed up as follows. Resource-allocation decisions are unavoidable in medicine: if so, then it would clearly be better, if it is possible and if it does not conflict with the demands of morality, that they should be based on some kind of rational principle. The only such principle considered so far is the market principle – that health care resources should be rationed by price, that their allocation should be governed by laws of supply and demand operating in a totally free market situation. But that principle, though rational in one sense and moral in that it insists on respect for human freedom of choice, seems to conflict with notions of social justice, which seem more important in this context. And attempts such as Brody's to make the notion of social justice consistent with a libertarian market-approach seem simply confused. If I am to justify my claim that rationing is ethically acceptable or even ethically desirable, therefore, I must seek to show that the market principle is not the only rational principle which might be used for allocating health care resources, nor even the only way in which economics may play a part in such allocation.

Rationality without the market

If we reject the market mechanism, do we also necessarily reject the idea of any kind of rational, and at the same time morally acceptable, principle for the allocation of health care? Some would argue that we do: that no principle of allocation can be both rational and morally acceptable, because any rational principle (and not only the market principle) must infringe the human right to health care. One such is the philosopher John Harris. Harris argues that the basic requirement of justice is 'that the continued existence and fundamental interests of each are valued as highly as those of any'.[6] It follows from this, he continues, that, in its allocation of those resources which affect such 'continued existence and fundamental interests', the state must not choose between individuals or permit choices to be made between them which affect their right to equal treatment. Hence it is unjust, because 'ageist', to select a younger person for renal dialysis rather than an older (when there is a shortage of dialysis machines which means that both cannot benefit from this treatment). The older person's continued existence is not being valued as highly as the younger person's.

The 'principle of equality', on which Harris relies in this argument, is indeed fundamental to the concept of justice: it is the basis for the objection that ability to pay should not be what decides whether one receives life-preserving or life-enhancing medical care, as it is on the pure market system. But the significance of the principle of equality should not be misunderstood. It implies that people should be treated in the same way *if there is no relevant difference between them.* When it comes to medical care, differential ability to pay for treatment is plainly not a relevant difference, so that discrimination on that basis would be unjust. The same would be true of discrimination on the grounds of gender, race, religion, social class, nationality, colour of hair, and so on. These distinctions between people plainly have no bearing on their entitlement to medical care when their medical needs are equal. Equally plainly, however, it does not follow from that that difference in medical needs is not a relevant difference when it comes to the allocation of health care resources.

Let us consider again, in the light of this, our imaginary case of the two patients with renal failure. In order to make the ethical points clearer, let us drastically simplify the situation, to the point of unreality: we shall suppose that only one dialysis machine is available, and that no possibility exists of other treatments, such as transplant surgery. One patient is a young man of, say, 27, who might expect at least 30 or 40 more years of (perhaps not very satisfactory) life if treated. The other is an elderly man of, say, 75, who might expect to live at most a year or two longer even if he were to receive dialysis. In one sense, of course, the medical needs of the two men are the same - both are suffering from the same condition to the same extent. This is the basis for Harris's claim that to discriminate between them would be unjust, 'ageist'.

Nevertheless, even Harris must accept that, in a situation such as I have described, only one of the two men can receive treatment: some discrimination between them is unavoidable. How can we discriminate without infringing the principle of equality? Harris's preferred solution to this dilemma is a lottery. 'If health professionals are forced by the scarcity of resources to choose', he says,[7] 'they should draw lots. They should not involve themselves in what amounts to unjust discrimination between individuals'. The beauty of the lottery, from his point of view, is that, being random, it applies equally to all patients, without regard to differences in their personal circumstances.

The idea that sometimes lotteries may be instruments of justice is not new. But are they instruments of justice in the allocation of medical care? Only if such things as relative age are irrelevant to a patient's deserts. In other contexts, relative age is indeed irrelevant, and in those contexts discrimination on grounds of age may reasonably be described as ageist. For instance, suppose a municipality has certain funds, which it can spend on only one of two projects - the construction of a day-centre at which old people can meet their friends and spend their time pleasantly and fruitfully, and the construction of a youth club at which young people can do the same. If the municipality chooses to build the youth club simply on the grounds that the young, as young, are more deserving, then it can justly be accused of ageism. The needs of the young in this regard are no greater than those of the old. A lottery would seem to be the only fair way of deciding the allocation of these funds.

Suppose, however, the choice was between building a training centre at which young people, just beginning on their working life, could learn a useful trade and so improve their chances of worthwhile and satisfying employment and building a centre at which retired people could learn interesting hobbies to increase their enjoyment of their remaining years. In a case like that, it might, to say the least, be less obvious that age was not a relevant difference, and that the need of the young for training which might enhance their many remaining years of life did not deserve more consideration than the need of the old for a leisure interest to enhance their much fewer remaining years. To discriminate in favour of the young in these circumstances might not seem so obviously ageist: indeed, it might be felt that to favour the old, or even to decide the matter by a mere toss of the coin (which might favour the old), would be to be guilty of an injustice towards the young.

Might not something similar be true in our imaginary medical case? If we provide dialysis for the older man, we are giving him one or two more years of life but denying many more years of life to the young man: and this is equally the case if we allow a lottery to decide and thereby risk the possibility that the older man might get the treatment. It might be felt that the fact that this decision (unlike the one about the training centre) involves matters of life and death makes an important difference ethically. By giving the treatment to the 27-year-old, we are not merely depriving the older man of the possibility of enhancing his life, we are depriving him of life itself. Are we not therefore infringing his right to life, surely the most basic right of all? Perhaps we are, but it must be said that if we decide the other way, even if it is as a result of a lottery, we are infringing the younger man's right to life. Tragically, in some situations in medicine we cannot avoid making choices between lives, and I cannot see how basing such choices on a toss of the coin is any more just than basing them on some more rational principle. The greatest objection to the method of rationing by queueing which prevails in so many areas of the British National Health Service is that it is unjust to the extent that it operates in an entirely random way.

Harris would no doubt say that it is less unjust to use a lottery because it does not involve putting a greater value on the life of a young man than on that of an old man. The relevance of this, however, depends on what precisely is meant by 'putting a greater value on'. If we valued the younger man's life more simply because he was more useful to society, more economically useful, for instance, then it would be unjust to prefer saving his life to that of the older man. It would be offensive to the human dignity of older people to suggest that their lives were worthless simply because they were no longer of much economic value. On the other hand, to save the life of a young person in preference to that of an old person because failure to save the young life would deprive that person of the years of life which the old person has already enjoyed might well seem to be simple justice. In other words, it is the value of the remaining life *to the patient himself or herself* which is the relevant sort of value in a case such as I have described.

It is undeniably true, as Harris hastens to point out, that the justice of discriminating in favour of the younger patient becomes less obvious in less extreme cases than those sketched in my example. If the two men were, not 27 and 75, but, say, 54 and 55, it would be far from obvious that justice required discrimination in favour of the younger man, so that in such circumstances a lottery might well be the only morally acceptable way of deciding who should get the treatment. I am happy to accept this: my point is not that there are always rational principles to enable us to decide on allocations, but that there can be such rational principles in some cases, and that, where there are, it is morally required that we base our decisions on them. It is plain to see that there are many cases in medicine in which no decision based on rational principles is possible. One case frequently cited is that of the allocation of beds in intensive care units, where there are no obvious rational grounds for deciding between patients, and certainly none which can be applied in the kind of pressurized atmosphere in which the medical staff in such units must necessarily operate. In such a case, the only sensible and morally acceptable way to make decisions is that which is actually used, namely to allocate beds on a purely random, 'first come, first served' basis. That this sometimes may lead to decisions which might appear, on calmer reflection, to be unjust is an unfortunate, but probably unavoidable, consequence of the fact that there is usually no time for such calm reflection.

Some people feel that the problem of finding acceptable rational principles for allocating health care resources is so insoluble that it would be morally better to avoid the need for allocation decisions as far as possible by providing more total resources for health care. It is certainly true that in some health care systems the total resource available is inadequate (this is true in my opinion of the British National Health Service at present). An increase in total resource available would reduce the need to make painful allocation decisions, whether based on rationing (in my sense) or on lotteries, and this would be a moral gain, simply because such decisions are often painful, however just.

Nevertheless, it is naive to think that resources for health care could ever be increased to such an extent that allocation-decisions could be avoided altogether. Resources are necessarily finite: an increase in national resources devoted to health care could only mean a corresponding decrease in those devoted to some other area of expenditure, and it is far from obvious that this would always be morally justifiable. Within health care provision itself, resources devoted to one field (kidney dialysis, for example) must necessarily be taken from another (say, paediatrics). However much resources devoted to healthcare might realistically be expected to be increased, therefore, allocation decisions cannot be avoided. Even if resources devoted to renal dialysis, for example, were increased to such an extent that the kind of problem indicated in my earlier example could always be avoided, there would still be the problem of whether it was just to allocate so much to this field at the expense of others. And it is much harder to find rational and morally justifiable principles to govern such macro-allocation decisions than it is to find similar principles for micro-allocation. Hence macro-allocations often have to be based on the lottery of political bargaining: the resulting decisions are no less painful for being irrational.

Mention of the fact that the resources available for health care are always, like all other resources, finite is a reminder that resource-allocation decisions inevitably involve the intrusion of economics into medical decision-making. Economics, after all, is often defined as the science or art of distributing scarce resources. If it is impossible for health professionals, hospital administrators and politicians to avoid making allocation-decisions as part of the fulfilment of their professional duties, then economics in this sense cannot be kept out of medicine. I have tried to show that it does not follow from this that allocation of health care resources needs to be based on free market principles, and that it is indeed morally unacceptable for it to be so based.

I have also referred in passing to another common basis for the fear of the intrusion of economic considerations. If we allow rationing - resource-allocation on rational principles - are we not necessarily committed to valuing human lives by purely economic criteria? After all, the resources which we allocate will nowadays almost certainly be *public* funds. This is most obviously the case with a system like the National Health Service, funded out of general taxation; but it is equally true of health insurance schemes, whether public or private. The patient's health care in all these cases will not be funded out of his or her own private resources. Rather, in virtually all contemporary systems of health care delivery, the patient's treatment will largely or entirely be funded out of the contributions of others - the premium-payers or tax-payers. There is a strong *prima facie* case, therefore, for saying that the fund-providers have a moral right to decide on the principles of resource-allocation. And it might be argued that the interests of those fund-providers will not be so much in the length or quality of remaining life for the patient *as valued by the patient himself or herself*, but rather in the economic value to the community of that life. The objection to the idea of rationing in these circumstances, therefore, might be that it would force health care providers to base their clinical decisions, not on the medical needs of individual patients, but on the economic needs of the wider community. And that would be seen, rightly, as contrary to the whole ethos of medicine.

Does this admittedly undesirable consequence necessarily follow from the acceptance of the moral need for rationing? It is certainly true that the institution of third-party payment does significantly alter what might be called the 'moral geography' of the medical situation. If (as would be virtually impossible in the context of expensive modern medicine) the individual were paying, out of his or her own private resources, the full costs of any medical treatment, then the relationship between individual patient and individual provider of health care would be contractual. The patient would be morally entitled to receive all the medical care which he or she required and could pay for, without regard to the requirements of anyone else. (It is, of course, possible that health care providers might refuse to enter into such contractual arrangements with individual patients, either because it was not in their interests or because they did not want to be prevented from doing what they could for other patients. In that case, there would be no such moral entitlement as I have described above).

But when, as is invariably and necessarily the case in modern medicine, patients as a group pool their funds in one way or another in order to be able to pay for the kinds of medical treatment which they may require, the moral geography changes. The providers of health care are funded by the collectivity, not by the individual patient with whom they may be dealing at a particular time, and therefore they are under some obligation to that collectivity to use its collective funds in accordance with the aims for which those funds were given. The patient, in turn, is entitled only to that treatment which is justified in terms of the aims of the collectivity. For an individual to take more than his or her share would be to do an injustice to the other members.

All this may sound suspiciously like an argument to justify rationing health care on the basis of the economic value of individual patients to the community. That would be so, however, only if the aims of the collectivities in question were to fund health care in order to promote collective economic efficiency alone. It is conceivable that private business-men might fund health care provision for their own employees with that kind of aim in mind: in that case, the employees would be entitled only to as much health care *funded on that basis* as was necessary to restore them to full economic effectiveness. But there would be nothing, of course, to prevent them from entering into some independent scheme of health-insurance (whether organised by the state or by private enterprise) which would provide supplementary health care for other purposes. The rationale for entering into such an insurance scheme, or for setting up a tax-funded National Health Service, is surely to provide by collective means for those health care needs which one is unable to provide from private resources. These health care needs will not be those which promote one's economic effectiveness (except incidentally), but those which must be satisfied if one is to live the kind of life one wishes to lead anyway. In other words, the aims of the collectivity will be that each member will have the most and the best health care for himself or herself which is attainable without harming the interests of other members. When the situation is described in that way, rationing can be seen to be a requirement of simple justice.

The QALY

One final objection to the notion of rationing needs to be considered before concluding. In recent years, discussions of rationing have tended to be bedevilled by the notion of the 'QALY', or 'Quality Adjusted Life Year', a concept devised by health-economists as a means of assessing the relative cost-effectiveness of different treatments. This notion is very thoroughly examined in the papers by Potts and Menzel in this volume but it may be helpful to summarize some points here in order to relate the notion of the QALY more closely to the argument of the present paper. The idea is that we can judge different treatments in terms of the number of years of extra life enjoyed by a successfully treated patient, multiplied by the quality of each of those years, as measured on a scale from 0 to 1. Thus, if a treated patient had 10 more years of life, each of which measured 0.5 on the quality scale, that treatment would have generated 5 QALYs. We can then arrive at the 'cost per QALY' for that treatment: suppose the treatment cost £1500, then the cost per QALY would be £300. Finally, we can compare this treatment with others in terms of their relative cost per QALY: if another treatment cost only £1000, but generated only two QALYs, then its cost per QALY, at £500, would be greater than that of the first treatment. It would be less cost-effective.

The QALY concept has been proposed as a basis for the rationing of health care, on grounds of cost: the fund-providers are assumed to want 'value for money', and measuring and comparing different treatments in terms of their cost per QALY is assumed to be an economically rational way of achieving this. Any form of rationing, of course, seeks to make the best possible use of finite resources, and in that sense seeks to achieve value for money. The difference between the various ways of rationing health care lies in the conception of what counts as the 'best possible use' of the relevant resources. For rationing by price, it is presumably that use which most completely equates supply with consumer demand. For rationing of the kind which I have argued for, it is that use of health care resources which maximizes distributive justice. Part of the problem for rationing on the basis of QALYs is that it is not clear whether what is meant in this context by 'value for money' embodies any such notions of morality or justice. The scale of qualities of life appears to be based on consumer preferences: the higher points on the scale are said to correspond to the greater number of expressed preferences. If so, then the best possible use of health care resources is that which comes closest to providing the kind of health care which most consumers would prefer.

But there are numerous problems with this. First, it is far from clear what consumers *would* prefer when it was their own life or well-being which was at stake. [For other views on this problem, see the papers by Potts and Menzel in this volume (eds)]. To take a favourite example of QALY-theorists, suppose I were told that my only chance of going on living was to have a heart transplant, but that I should probably not live for more than a year or two after the operation in rather restricted conditions. Even so, I might well prefer resources to be used to provide me with transplant surgery, even if the same money could pay for several hip-replacements which would add many years of high-quality life to their recipients. The same might well be true if it was not I who needed the transplant but someone else whose fate I care about. The preferences of different consumers of healthcare would almost inevitable conflict with each other, *unless*, of course, those preferences were based not on self-interested wishes, but on altruistic concern for the well-being of others.

This reveals the second problem in the QALY concept. The only workable way of assessing the relative quality of life resulting from different treatments would be one based, not on subjective consumer preferences, but on objective notions of justice. But such notions of justice do not lend themselves to the kind of precise quantitative assessment which is required if the QALY concept is to function in the manner its inventors intended.

How, for instance, can we precisely compare the moral worth of saving the life of a heart patient by means of transplant surgery with that of enhancing the mobility of an old person by means of a hip-replacement? How can we even place these two things in the same scales? Any comparison between them must be based on *qualitative* judgments, not on simple mechanical conceptions of cost-effectiveness.

This brings us to the most fundamental objection of all to the notion of rationing health care. If morally acceptable (let alone morally required) rationing requires a basis in principles which are both rational and moral, then how are we to arrive at such principles? We live in a plural society, in which there are a number of competing value-systems. We may believe, for instance, that life ought in general to be prolonged where possible, but we may differ radically in our views about the permissible exceptions to that rather vague general rule. Is it morally justifiable to utilize resources in cash, equipment, time, energy and skill to preserve the lives of very premature infants or older people with failing hearts, if those resources could be used instead to provide hip-replacements or better care for the mentally ill? Or would it, on the other hand, be morally monstrous to use resources to improve the lives of those whose continued existence is not threatened when they could be used instead to save more lives? It might well be felt that our moral intuitions, at least in contemporary society, are not clear enough to allow us to settle such questions. But if so, it might be argued, they cannot provide us with acceptable rational principles to decide on resource-allocation.

This counsel of despair ought to be resisted. It is of course the case, as I have admitted earlier in this paper, that there are many resource-allocation decisions which it is in practice or even in principle impossible to base on rational moral criteria, and for those some form of lottery seems to be the only possible foundation. But given that considerations of justice are inseparable from health care decisions, it seems a mere abdication of responsiblity to assume in advance that any given resource-allocation decision will be of that nature. There is a moral imperative to at least seek for some rational moral principle on which the decision can be based. In view of the inescapable fact of moral pluralism and uncertainty in our society, there seems only one way in which that quest can be pursued. A general public debate needs to be instigated on the ends which we think it right for our health care system to achieve. The outcome of that debate, to the extent that it was clear, would only, of course, represent a provisional moral consensus rather than the establishment of permanent and objective moral values. But even that would surely be preferable to allowing decisions affecting human lives and well-being to be left to the subjective values of individual doctors or managers, to the political clout of particular specialties, or to the emotional appeal of certain kinds of case to passing public sentiment. Given that we cannot do everything for everybody, we ought at least to see if it is possible to use our resources to help those who most deserve help.

Notes

1. Norman Daniels (1985), ch. 1. (The description of health care as 'special' is also found elsewhere in Daniels' writings).
2. Baruch Brody, 'Health care for the haves and have-notes: toward a just basis of distribution', in Shelp (ed.) (1981), pp. 151-59. For Brody's current views, see his paper in this volume.
3. Brody, *op cit.*, p. 155.
4. Brody, *op cit.*, p. 157.
5. *Id., ibid.*
6. John Harris, 'Rationing life: quality or justice?': quotations are given from the version of this paper given at the 1987 meeting of the Association for Legal and Social Philosophy. Typescript p. 11.
7. Harris, *op. cit.*, typescript pp. 13f.

4 The QALY and why it should be resisted

S.G. Potts

The QALY (Quality Adjusted Life Year) was first discovered a decade or so ago by Anglo-American academics stalking the hinterlands of health economics, where it led a quiet existence and posed a threat to no-one. Various attempts were made to capture it and put it to work in the task of guiding health policy, but these expeditions generally fizzled out with little result (Weinstein and Stason, 1977). In recent years, however, a determined British effort has had more success, and has lead to the explicit employment of the QALY by some British administrators in making key resource allocation decisions. In this paper I shall argue that in this environment the QALY is a far from innocuous and helpful work-beast: that, on the contrary, it is dangerous in the extreme - a killer. It must be opposed and eradicated now, at this early stage in its career, before it becomes more firmly established.

In order to understand why the QALY is so attractive to British policy makers, and why it has so far been largely ignored by their counterparts in the United States, I shall briefly outline the structure of health service funding in Britain. The portion of Britain's health care provided by private medicine has definitely increased in recent years, with the active encouragement of the Thatcher government; but it remains true that the National Health Service still provides much more, perhaps 85-90%. The budget of the N.H.S. is massive. It employs nearly a million people. Yet, expressed as a percentage of the nation's G.N.P. it amounts to a little over half of what is spent in the United States, and about two thirds of what is spent in most Western European countries. Given this level of funding, it is not surprising that a great emphasis is placed upon the notion of efficiency, not least by the government itself.

For purposes of Health Service administration, the country is divided into seventeen Regions, each overseen by a Regional Health Authority (RHA). This body runs the primary care services, the community facilities, the district general hospitals, and, in conjunction with the university medical schools, the teaching hospitals, of which there are approximately two per region. Each RHA is allocated an overall budget depending on the demographic characteristics of the population it serves. It then determines how that budget is allocated between and within the various divisions of the services it runs. There are therefore three main levels of macroallocational decision:

a. What proportion of the GNP goes to the NHS.
b. How to divide it up between the regions.
c. How to distribute the region budget among various services.

The first has been the subject of hotly contested political debate for years and looks set to remain so. The second level might appear a more straightforward matter of demographics, but the setting up of a body called the Resource Allocation Working Party (RAWP) intended to secure a more equitable distribution of the health service budget around the country, triggered arguments which, though less public, are no less heated. This is partly because of disagreement about the statistics used, but more particularly because redistribution involves freezing or cutting the budgets of some previously favoured regions.

It is, however, the third level of decision that concerns me now. The results of decisions at the first two levels determine how big the overall regional budget will be. Because the NHS is built around the central premise of universal access at the time of need, unconstrained by ability to pay, the demand for medical services has always been larger than the supply that this limited budget has been able to secure. This is the essential difference between health care in Britain and the United States - the former has open access for people but a closed budget, and the latter has an open-ended budget but access is available only to those who can pay or carry insurance. Explicit rationing has therefore always been a feature of the British system, while the primary problems in the United States are now cost-containment and securing access for the uninsured. The American system simply does not generate a requirement for a procedure to ration resources in the same way that Britain's does.

For RHAs beset by competing claims from different services, all with obvious merit, the problems of distributing their budgets have proved very difficult. Imagine a meeting of one such RHA. They are approached by the orthopaedic surgeons, who are armed with statistics about the ever-lengthening waiting lists for elective surgery, especially for hip replacements, and who plead that the region employ another consultant, enlarge the nursing team, and assign the speciality another ward. In the lobby, they meet representatives of the renal unit, who are pressing the RHA to devote more funds to run and maintain another dialysis machine, without which more preventable deaths from end stage renal failure will occur. Also waiting their turn are the cardiologists who want to expand their pacemaker implantation programme to meet increasing demands as the population ages.

Faced with stark choices between these and other merit-worthy claims, the RHA members, naturally enough, look around for some kind of decision procedure to help them arbitrate. If these were business decisions they might prove difficult, but not, ultimately, morally perplexing, because an economic decision procedure, namely cost-benefit analysis (CBA), is generally applicable, and more or less universally accepted. Costs and benefits are calculated in dollar terms, and after discounting procedures for costs borne or benefits realised in the future (of which more later), a simple calculation is made and the various competing candidate projects compared for efficiency in cost-benefit terms. When the transactions involved are complex it may be difficult to measure all the relevant costs and benefits, and there may be controversy about whether particular expenses or gains should be included in the analysis, but there is at least common acknowledgement that the decision procedure itself is valid.

In health care, however, the difficulty of rendering gains in dollar terms is notorious, and so severe as to make cost-benefit analysis simply unworkable. The health economist then suggests cost-effectiveness analysis (CEA), in which gains are expressed in some *non*-financial terms, such as number of lives saved, or years of life expectancy added, or serious injuries prevented. A problem immediately arises from the difficulty of comparing these various measures, however, which does not apply to cost-benefit analysis, where the dollar is the universal unit. How can project A, which saves lives, be compared with project B, which prevents disability? Only if there is a generally accepted common currency in which various different types of medical benefit can be compared on the same scale. Professor Alan Williams of York, among others, has advocated the QALY as a strong candidate to fulfil this role (Williams, 1985. Maynard, 1986) Here, it seems, is the answer to the need so acutely felt by the RHAs for a way to rank the competing claims made upon their resources in some order of priority, and to do so not by imposing an arbitrary fiat or by succumbing to the power of the strongest lobby, but by employing an objectively valid and universally applicable measure of outcome in a cost-effectiveness analysis. How does it work?

The nature of the beast

Professor Williams uses a scale developed largely by Rachel Rosser (Rosser and Watts, 1974. Kind, Williams and Rosser, 1982. Rosser, 1984), which measures quality of life by combining the values of two variables: distress (by which is meant primarily pain) and disability (by which is meant primarily the limitation placed upon a person's activity range by a reduced physical mobility). Distress is assessed on a scale of four grades, from A (no distress), through B (mild) and C (moderate) to D (severe). Disability is assessed on an eight grade scale, from I (no disability) to VIII (unconscious) [see Tables 1 and 2].

Table 4.1
Grades of disability

Grade 1	No disability
Grade II	Slight social disability
Grade III	Severe social disability, slight impairment of performance at work, or both; able to do all except heavy housework
Grade IV	Choice of work or performance at work severely limited, housewives and old people to do only light housework, but able to go out shopping
Grade V	Unable to undertake any paid employment, unable to continue any education: old people confined to home except for escorted outings and short walks and unable to shop, housewives able to perform only a few simple tasks.
Grade VI	Confined to chair or wheelchair or able to move only with support.
Grade VII	Confined to bed.
Grade VIII	Unconscious.

Table 4.2
Grades of distress

Grade A	None
Grade B	Mild
Grade C	Moderate
Grade D	Severe

There are thus thirty-two combinations of these two variables. Rosser, Williams and their colleagues constructed a valuation matrix by asking a group of 70 respondents to rate each combination on a scale defined by two points, full health at a value of 1, and death at a value of 0, and by taking the median rating for this group (see Table 3).

Table 4.3
Valuation matrix

		Distress Rating			
		A	B	C	D
	I	1.001	0.995	0.990	0.967
	II	0.990	0.986	0.973	0.932
	III	0.980	0.972	0.956	0.912
Disability	IV	0.964	0.956	0.942	0.870
Rating	V	0.946	0.935	0.900	0.700
	VI	0.875	0.845	0.680	0
	VII	0.677	0.564	0	-1.486
	VIII	-1.028	n/a	n/a	n/a

[Source for tables: Teeling Smith 1985, p.15]

Valuations of all the various combinations can then be combined with life expectancy data to yield a composite measure reflecting both duration and quality of life. The unit in which this measure is expressed is the QALY, the quality adjusted life year. A year spent at full health rates as a gain of one QALY: a year spent with a disability rating of VI and a distress rating of C represents a gain of 0.68 QALYs. The QALY can thus be defined:

> **A quality adjusted life year or QALY is a year of life expectancy whose value has been adjusted for the anticipated level of distress and disability at which it will be lived, in such a way that it can be expressed in terms of an equivalent number of years spent at full health.**

Applications

The QALY is meant to be a universal unit of effectiveness of medical (and other) interventions, which can be combined with estimates of the cost of such interventions to construct cost-effectiveness (or, more accurately, cost *utility*) analyses. For instance, if a medical intervention saves a patient's life to yield a life expectancy of ten years spent, on average, at a distress rating of C and a disability rating of VI (yielding a combined valuation of 0.68), it generates 6.8 QALYs. If this intervention costs $6,800, its cost-effectiveness can be expressed in terms of cost-per-QALY gained, the figure in this case being $1,000 per QALY. The intervention can then be compared with others in cost effectiveness terms.

Williams has made these calculations for a number of medical interventions, mainly one-off surgical procedures employing high technology (and therefore costing a lot). He has ranked these procedures in terms of cost-effectiveness, yielding league tables (see table 4) which correspond fairly well to similar tables produced by other workers.

Table 4.4
Ranking of procedures by cost-effectiveness

Most cost effective:	Pacemaker implantation Hip replacement Aortic valve replacement
Intermediate:	Coronary artery bypass graft* Coronary angioplasty* Renal transplantation
Least cost effective:	Heart transplantation Home haemodialysis Hospital haemodialysis

[source: a composite of three tables in Williams, 1985, p.3281]

*Widely varying cost-effectiveness, depending on extent of coronary artery disease, and nature of symptoms.

Differentiations *within* categories are made too: for example, pacemaker implantation for complete heart block is more cost-effective than the same procedure undertaken for sick sinus syndrome; and coronary artery bypass grafting is more cost-effective for patients with severe angina and triple vessel disease than it is for those with severe angina and single vessel disease.

Returning now to the context of our fictional RHA meeting, we can imagine the board producing its health economist who has constructed a cost-effectiveness league table on which the various projects competing for support are ranked. The RHA director then turns to each of the supplicants in turn, saying to the orthopaedic surgeons, 'Your hip transplants are very cost effective. We approve your project and will fund it in full.' And to the cardiologists, 'Your pacemaker implantations and valve replacements are very cost effective, your bypass grafts less so, and your heart transplants least of all. We will not increase your overall funding, and suggest that you transfer resources within your budget to the more cost-effective interventions.' Finally, to the nephrologists, 'None of your procedures is cost-effective. We propose to reduce your funding, rather than increase it. We may cut your department entirely.'

Objections

There is an intuitive repulsion for any RHA which could conduct its affairs in this manner, which, I shall argue, arises from a number of fatal defects in the QALY and its employment in cost-effectiveness analysis. Before considering them it is worth pointing out, however, that the QALY may have a certain limited application in medical decision-making, but only if it is disconnected from any attempt at a cost-effectiveness analysis. It may well be possible to use some of the QALY calculations to help choose between different treatments available for an individual patient or type of patient. Suppose for example we can show that for the average patient with moderate angina and left main vessel disease, coronary artery bypass grafting generates substantially more QALYs than medical management, while the reverse is true for angina patients in a different subgroup. Suppose further that mortality statistics for the two treatments in these subgroups are broadly similar. It is reasonable to conclude that cardiologists can be guided (but not directed) by these statistics in advising their patients about the most appropriate treatment. This, however, is an uncontroversial use of QALY statistics without major ethical implications; representing nothing more than the attempt to supply something more than bare survival data in lending statistical support to the advice cardiologists give their patients.

It is clear, however, that the advocates of QALYs intend for them a role much wider than this, and it is the ethical implications of these wider uses that prompt the raising of the objections listed below.

I. *Objections to the techniques of cost-effectiveness analysis itself*

Cost-effectiveness analysis is often presented, especially in medical circles, as if it were a problem-free objective methodology, one which would have extensive applicability if only we could agree on the units by which to measure effectiveness. This is a misleading picture which ignores or significantly underestimates the seriousness of problems inherent in the method. I shall mention just two of these problems, though there are more.

a. *Difficulties in cost calculation*

Cost calculation is generally presented as difficult but feasible, the difficulty being essentially a practical one arising from the financial complexity of medical establishments and their operations. But a key question is too easily missed - *what* costs are to be included? This question applies at several levels. At the most general level, we can ask whether the appropriate costs are:

- only costs borne by the RHA commissioning the analysis, or
- those costs borne by the NHS as a whole, or
- all costs borne by public, tax-funded services, or
- all costs borne by public services, private agencies, and individuals.

Furthermore, what of the non-financial costs, the quanta of private griefs and social disruptions? Even if these *can* be measured in financial terms, are they to be included or not?

Answers to these questions are not provided by the techniques of cost-effectiveness analysis itself. The answers are value-laden, especially since analyses carried out on the basis of different answers can, in principle, yield significantly different implications for health policy, and therefore *very* significantly different implications for individual lives. For example, if the answer to the question 'What costs?' is 'All those borne by public tax-funded services', then the implications of medical treatment for patients' future employment prospects will figure very large in the calculations. If life-saving intervention A restores young but moribund individuals to a level of functioning where they can work and support their families, while intervention B, which otherwise costs the same and is equally life-saving, cannot restore employability, then intervention A will gain a higher priority on cost-effectiveness grounds. If resources are not sufficient to support both programmes, then patients needing intervention B will die simply because they are unemployable.

The same question can be asked at a more specific level too. When considering the cost-effectiveness of a particular procedure, should we include:

- only the costs of the procedure itself, or
- the costs of the procedure, together with the costs of follow-up support plus treatment of complications, etc, or
- all the short and long term costs of both treatment *and* non-treatment?

Thus, when assessing the cost-effectiveness of such low-priority treatments as heart transplants, are we to include in the calculations all the costs of non-treatment? Heart transplantation and anti-rejection treatment may be expensive in absolute terms (so many thousands of dollars for the surgery and post-operative care, so many thousands for the anti-rejection drugs); but what about in comparison with the only available alternative, which is intensive medical, nursing and social support for the remainder of the patient's life?

A proper cost-effectiveness analysis for health care interventions should at the very least consider all the short-term and long term costs of both treatment and non-treatment, and all the medical and social costs borne by tax-funded agencies. Most such analyses stop short of this however, and usually because the complexity of such comprehensive cost-counting is so dauntingly great. But when lives are at stake, the limitations placed upon the class of costs to be included require a much stronger justification than mere difficulty of calculation. In the absence of such clear-cut and well-justified criteria to determine which costs to include and which may legitimately be excluded, cost-effectiveness analysis will inevitably be somewhat arbitrary. When applied to health care this means that some people will die and others live because of arbitrary and insupportable accounting decisions. An example might make this clearer. In Britain the Health Service and Social Security, which provides support to the unemployed and their dependents, used to be both sub-divisions of the same Government department, the DHSS, but their budgets were quite separate. Thus cost-effectiveness analysis could include either the costs to the health service division of the DHSS, or the costs to the DHSS as a whole. The choice adopted would affect the outcome of the analysis. Why should the implementation of health programmes, a life-or-death question for patients needing a 'low priority' treatment, depend in this way on the structure of government bureaucracy?

b. *Discounting*

Even if agreement could be reached on the right measure of effectiveness and the proper costs to include, the procedure itself is still not without problems. Discounting, for example, remains a controversial practice even in strictly economic applications of cost-effectiveness analysis. Future costs cannot be compared directly with present ones, because any money not spent immediately can be invested to earn interest. Therefore, in comparing two programmes which cost the same and realise the same gains, it will make a difference whether the programme accrues costs in the present or in the future, with the latter being preferred, to a degree dependent on the chosen discount rate. Similar arguments apply to benefits, to maintain parity with costs. In cost-effectiveness analysis using QALYs, this has the counterintuitive result that a QALY gained in the present is worth more financially than a QALY gained in the future. Economists argue that discounting does not systematically undervalue future costs or benefits, and that any disparity is only apparent. Even if they are right, there remains the question of the value to be assigned to the discount rate. Different surveys use different values, ranging from 0 to 10%, the most common values being in the range 4 to 6%.

Again, though, the results of CEA-based priority rankings may vary significantly depending on the chosen discount rate, and any disparity between the chosen discount rate and the real behaviour of the economy. Why should people's lives depend in this way on the behaviour of interest rates and the accuracy of our guesses at them?

Many surveys of the applicability of cost-effectiveness analysis in medical contexts give a nod to these and other defects in their procedure, but usually follow up this grudging admission with an 'escape' clause, best represented by the words of the economists themselves:

> At present, using the approach or process of CEA/CBA [cost-effectiveness analysis/cost-benefit analysis] in decision-making may be more helpful than the rigid and formal application of CEA/CBA study results in healthcare program decisions.
> (Office of Technology Assessment, 1980, p.3)

and

> The principal value of formal cost-effectiveness analysis in health care is that it forces one to be explicit about the beliefs and values that underlie allocation decisions. Opposing points of view can be clarified in terms of specific disagreements over assumptions, probability estimates or value trade-offs.
> (Weinstein and Stason, 1977, p.721)

It may well be that some economists well recognise the deficiencies in applications of CEA to health care: but it is certainly not true of all of them, and still less of those policy-makers they advise. If it really were no more than a clarificatory exercise designed to bring out implicit assumptions in resource allocation, employing CEA would indeed be useful and innocuous. All too often, however, CEA is explicitly presented as a tool for setting priorities in health policy.

Witness:

> Alternative programs or services are then ranked, from the lowest value of this cost-per-effectiveness ratio to the highest, and selected from the top until available resources are exhausted.
> (Weinstein and Stason, 1977, p.717)

or, more specifically,

> Resources need to be redeployed ... to procedures for which the benefits to patients are high in relation to the costs, such as the insertion of pacemakers for heart block [etc.] *These treatments should take priority* over additional facilities for patients needing kidney transplants [etc.] ... for which the costs per QALY gained are higher.
> (Williams, 1985, p.329. [emphasis added])

Protestations of innocence, of indulging only in clarification, are a sham. CEA was introduced as a health policy tool and is increasingly being used in that role without sufficient regard to its inadequacies.

II. *Objections to the QALY itself*

Having attacked the enterprise of CEA as applied to medicine, why say anything about the QALY? Because it is the introduction of the QALY into CEA that has made CEA attractive to medical policy-makers, and has allowed them to use it in their planning whereas they previously rejected it as unworkable. The defects intrinsic to the QALY and its employment therefore need to be spelt out.

a. *The grading of disability and distress*

The two scales of disability and distress are presented very starkly in Tables 1 and 2 above, leaving unanswered a number of questions, such as:

- Why are there only two scales?
- Why are *these* the only two scales used?
- Why are they sub-divided into eight and four grades respectively?
- Why not more or fewer? Why *these* eight and *these* four grades?
- Who does the grading?

These questions reflect unease at the suggestion that an individual's quality of life can be reduced to a score on two simplistic scales. The artificial nature of the scales is evident from the assumption that it is possible to be in severe distress and yet suffer no disability at all (i.e. disability rating I, distress rating D; valued at 0.967). Their incompleteness is evident too: where does someone's artistic ability come in? What about the inspiration given by the struggle of handicapped people to overcome their limitations? Or the intellectual abilities displayed by someone like Stephen Hawking, the Cambridge University Professor who is a world leader in theoretical physics despite being seriously disabled and distressed by a crippling neurological disease?

Disability and distress obviously are components in an individual's quality of life: but they are by no means the only components, and it is far from clear that the scales suggested are accurate indices by which to measure them. This is a serious problem for the QALY as currently conceived. It is possible however, that much more sophisticated scales and measures may be developed which give better overall assessments of the quality of life, so that these deficiencies may be potentially correctable, if only in part. Other objections however, expose those defects in the QALY and its operation which are not correctable at all, however sophisticated the measurement becomes.

b. *The valuation method*

In constructing the valuation matrix, Williams, and before him Rosser, used the responses of 70 respondents. Who are they? How are they chosen? The question is crucial, because, as Williams acknowledges, different people will make different valuations. He says:

> The respondents included 10 doctors, all of whom appeared to have much greater aversion to disability and distress than the population at large; they would therefore overvalue reductions in disability and distress compared with the rest of the population.
> (Williams, 1985, p. 327)

A decision therefore has to be made as to the nature of the group whose valuations are solicited. Should they be

- representative of the population affected by the implementation of the programme, or
- representative of those who will fund the health programme (the taxpayers), or
- representative of those who will operate it, or
- representative of the population at large?

Williams does not explicitly answer this question, but the implicit response seems to be the last; he wants the valuing group to be representative of the population at large. This sounds nice and democratic, but it is not, for the inevitable consequence is that the fate of people with a particular illness is determined by the preferences of people who are, on the whole, healthy. No allowance is made for the possibility that the valuations people make might *change* when they fall ill. Even the illness-averse doctors remarked on by

Williams may revise their valuations once they are in the patient's role. There is operating here a kind of dictatorship of the healthy, in which the fate of ill people is determined by the aversion of healthy people to a distress and disability they do not themselves experience.

Without a satisfactory justification of the choice of valuing group, the construction of the valuation matrix will be too arbitrary to provide anything like the firm basis that QALY-based assessments require.

c. *Ageism*

Using QALYs in health-care decisions will result in a systematic discrimination in favour of the young. Ageism is built in to the system. Consider a group of patients of various ages, all with an illness which will kill them if untreated. Suppose a treatment exists which could cure them, returning them to full health and giving them the same life expectancy as the rest of the population (say 70), but that resources are limited so that only half of the patients can receive it. For a 20-year old, the treatment generates 50 QALYs; for a 50-year old it generates 20 QALYs at the same cost. On cost-effectiveness grounds then, the patient's age should be a principal, if not determining, feature, in selection for treatment.

d. *Racism and sexism*

While ageism is inherent in the system, sexism and racism are contingently related to it. Consider the case of renal transplantation for end stage renal failure secondary to diabetes. It is anticipated that any kidney grafted into such a patient will in all probability also undergo diabetic nephropathy, so that after a certain number of years renal function will decline to a level where dialysis and/or a further transplant will be necessary. Suppose further that statistics show that graft survival is longer in men than in women, and in whites than blacks. Giving a transplant to a white man therefore generates more QALYs than giving it to a black woman, other things being equal, and if patient selection is required because of a scarcity of resources, then cost-effectiveness criteria will justify choosing on the basis of race and gender.

It might well be that for other interventions race and gender differences work the other way, so that for example black men are the preferred candidates for pancreatic transplantation, and white women most appropriate for hip replacements. Nevertheless the use of QALYs in resource allocations will regularly justify such race and gender-based discrimination whenever the statistics show that race and gender are relevant to prognosis.

e. *Distributive justice*

As well as the injustice of the inherent ageism, and the contingent racism and sexism, injustice is manifest too in the matter of the distribution of the QALYs produced by a proposed health programme. Because the aim of the system is to maximize the gain in QALYs, regardless of who gets them, it is quite probable that a programme will be preferred which gives twenty-five QALYs to one person instead of one QALY each to a group of twenty people. Suppose, for example, there is a choice between funding a chemotherapy programme which, it is anticipated, will save the lives of patients with leukaemia, allowing them on average a further twenty-five years of fully healthy life; and funding an angioplasty programme, which will extend the healthy lives of those with coronary atheroma but only by one year or so. Suppose that saving each leukaemic patient costs as much as treating twenty-five heart patients. Reliance on QALY-based CEA alone will dictate the choice of the chemotherapy programme, so that all the resources are poured into the treatment of one patient, and twenty-five other patients go untreated.

To an extent the leukaemic patients resemble 'utility monsters', those bugbears described in such frightening terms by objectors to utilitarian moral theory; and not surprisingly, for the aim of health policy-makers to maximize QALYs is closely analogous to the aim of utilitarian moralists to maximize utility, and shares many of its defects. These arise primarily from the separation in each case of the maximands (i.e. the things to be maximized), whether QALYs or utility, from the individual lives that bear them. Individual lives drop out of consideration in both systems, so that the way benefits are distributed between lives becomes irrelevant. Under this system, the aim of medicine is to make the output of QALYs as high as possible. Individual patients are important only to the extent that their continued existence adds to the sum total of QALYs gained. To use an analogy developed by the British philosopher Bernard Williams, individual patients do not matter any more than individual gasoline tanks matter in the measurement of a nation's gasoline consumption.

f. *Propensity to justify killing*

In the valuation matrix Williams uses, some levels of disability and distress give life such a low quality that it is valued at almost nothing (that is, nearly as bad as death), zero (that is, equivalent to death) or negatively (that is, worse than death). These unfortunates generally require considerable expense to support their continued existence. To go on living is not just a burden to the patients or their families, but to the health care system and the society which supports it.

One very cost-effective approach to those with a negative quality of life would be to kill them by a quick, cheap, and painless injection. Such an action would not generate any positive QALYs, but would minimize the continuing accumulation of negative QALYs at great expense. For those whose lives are of zero quality, killing would neither generate nor save any QALYs, but would prevent a continuing drain on resources. For those whose quality of life is low, but positive, the position is slightly different. To continue supporting them will generate few QALYs at high cost. Simply to withdraw that support will eliminate costs but may well lead to considerable suffering (i.e. an accumulation of negative QALYs) before death. Killing them, on the other hand, will also eliminate the costs of further support, while avoiding the generation of any negative QALYs.

On cost-effectiveness grounds then, killing could become not merely permitted in the health care system, but elevated to the level of a high-priority intervention. This is, in part, acknowledged by one of the advocates of such QALY-based CEA, when he says:

> But [the fact that some states of survival have a negative score] could, eventually, argue in favour of voluntary euthanasia.
> (Teeling Smith 1985, p.23)

The QALY proponent who feels uncomfortable with this conclusion might exclude the possibility by using an independently-grounded opposition to killing: but this tactic can only work in conjunction with the maintenance of a strong distinction between killing and letting die, or perhaps an appeal to the doctrine of double effect. Only by employing such a distinction can the supporter of the QALY argue that the denial of funding to such 'low priority' interventions as renal dialysis, with the foreseeable deaths of identifiable individuals, is significantly different in moral terms from active killing for those with a low, zero or negative quality of life. It seems unlikely that such utility-minded people as the proponents of QALYs and CEA will readily accept the need to rely on such a distinction; but without it their system cannot work.

Alternatives

Whenever health economists are challenged on these and other grounds, the response they produce, reasonably enough, is to argue that allocation decisions must be made somehow, that they are too often made on implicit grounds which are just as deeply flawed, and if QALY-based CEA is rejected, a better alternative must be suggested.

In leading the philosophical opposition to QALYs in Britain, John Harris has argued that justice in allocation decisions will only be done if a lottery or randomization procedure is employed in selecting between competing candidates for treatment (Harris 1986). However he argues for this only at the level of micro-allocational choices between individuals, and gives no alternative to the use for which QALYs were originally mooted, namely macro-allocational choices between different health programmes.

It is possible though to extend the argument from justice to this higher level. If it is unjust to discriminate against individuals because their illnesses are expensive to treat, it is also unjust to discriminate against groups of individuals on the same grounds. When resources are inadequate to treat everybody, there is an alternative way to allocate them, based on the premise that an individual's chance of being treated should be the same whatever illness he has. Suppose that in a given population there are 100 people who can be restored to good health and full life expectancy by aortic valve replacement, at a cost of $10,000 each (a total cost of $1 million). There are also 50 people who can be restored to good health and full life expectancy by renal dialysis and transplantation at a cost of $30,000 each (a total cost of $1.5 million). Suppose further that the health authority only has $1 million to spend on these two programmes. If priorities are dictated by a QALY-based CEA, then all the available funds will be directed to the valve replacement programme, so that all the heart patients and none of the kidney patients will be treated. A total of 100 lives will be saved.

If we stipulate that an individual's chance of being treated when treatment is not available for all should be the same whatever illness he has, then it works out that with a budget of $1 million, we can afford to treat 40% of each group (i.e. 40 heart patients and 20 kidney patients). The selection of patients from each group is then to be conducted by randomization or lottery procedures. The total number of lives saved is lower, at 60, on this allocation, it is true, but none of the untreated can claim that they have been unjustly discriminated against. The forty extra deaths in this allocation could be labelled, bluntly, as the price of justice. I fear for the consequences if we regard it as too high a price to pay.

5 QALYs, quality of life and rationing

Paul T. Menzel

According to a very controversial view in health economics the proper goal of health services is to create as many years of healthy life as possible. For its unit of a year of healthy life, this view constructs the notion of a QALY (quality adjusted life year). The moral justification for using such a unit to measure the productivity of investing resources in health care is the innocent-sounding claim that for all of us alike, a year of healthy life is equally valuable.[1]

It is hard to overemphasize how helpful this conceptual unit, a QALY, really is in health policy. Should we spend more, for instance, on hip replacements or kidney dialysis? Or save more lives with dialysis or coronary by-pass surgery?[2] With QALYs we get an answer: we can compare quality improvements with lifesaving, and saving a life of one quality with saving a life of another. One commentator ventures that by the next century the use of QALYs will be 'just as...accepted and central...as controlled clinical trials' are now.[3] Rationing decisions in health care will gain an at least somewhat objective productivity dimension.

Should we welcome such a development? In this essay I will end up defending in a very qualified fashion the half of QALY reasoning that strikes many people as most objectionable, adjusting for quality of life (QOL).[4]

1. How quality adjustment works

The first thing to get clear is just how QALYs work. A common misperception is to think that their use disadvantages people with low QOL. In one respect it does, but overall it does not. Precisely because of QOL adjustment, non-lifesaving improvements from low QOL get more weight in any competition with lifesaving measures than they would otherwise have.

To be sure, QOL adjustment weakens the competitive position of a patient with renal failure, e.g., in trying to get dialysis. If her QOL is 0.6, she would only gain 6.0 QALYs for her 10 years on $30,000/year of lifesaving dialysis, and the resulting $50,000/QALY cost would undoubtedly place her treatment in a relatively low priority position in any rationing.[5] She will more likely lose out to hip replacements than if her benefit was counted as 10 unadjusted life years.

But in another respect she would gain by quality adjustment. Suppose a kidney transplant would raise her quality of life from 0.6 to 0.8 for 10 years; it would produce 2.0 QALYs beyond dialysis. At a cost, say, of $20,000 for the transplant and $40,000 for subsequent cyclosporin ($4000/year for 10 years), her roughly $30,000/QALY gain puts her claim for a transplant in better stead against other services than if we ignored her jump in QOL. Hip replacements, of course, also gain because of quality adjustment. Though no lifesaving may be involved at all, 15 years at 1.0 instead of 0.9 constitutes a 1.50 QALY gain from just an $8000 operation.[6] Thus quality adjustment cuts both ways for those with low enough QOL to affect allocations: it benefits patients in competing for quality enhancing services, but it disadvantages them in competing for lifesaving ones.

How does one get any of these numerical quality adjustment ratings to begin with, and does that process show that they are morally important to incorporate into health policy? The actual methods used by health economists are detailed in the Appendix.

The major moral argument for QOL adjustment, that it is people themselves who at least implicitly quality rank their own lives, is supposedly based in these methods: we get quality adjustment ratios by consulting the very sort of people likely to be affected by the rationing decisions that result.[7]

But our main moral reservation about QOL adjustment emerges right at this point: given the questions we might ask people in order to construct their QOL rankings, can their answers be properly construed as constituting consent to the rationing priorities that quality adjustment generates?[8]

2. Your life is all you've got, no matter what its quality

Suppose you yourself prefer a shorter, healthier life over a longer less healthy one. If you have expressed that preference in comparing two versions of life, *both for yourself*, have you in any way consented to saving the healthier life of one person rather than the lower quality life of *another*?

It's not clear. Suppose you later turn out to be an accident victim who could survive, though paraplegic, while someone else could achieve more complete recovery. Each of you 'wants to go on living...equally fervently,' so why should society save the one of you with the 'most QALYs on offer'?[9] Your preference for normal health over lower quality longer life in your own case is not by itself a statement that paraplegic life should someday take second place in a competition between saving two different people. Of course you yourself preferred a QOL with complete recovery to one with paraplegia. But you never therein admitted that when life itself is on the line, a life with paraplegia is any less valuable to the person whose life it is than life without that disability. For all we know, *compared to death*, your paraplegic life could still be as valuable to you as anyone else's 'better' life is to them.

If QALYs are to cut the moral mustard here, people simply have to be agreeing to something further when they express those initial quality judgments from which the numerical QOL rankings are extrapolated. Let's look at four different questions used to establish these numerical rankings:

Time Trade-Off How much shorter a life in good health would you find preferable to a longer lifetime with the disability or distress you are ranking?[10] (If 10 percent shorter, then QOL is 0.9.)

Standard Gamble What risk of death would you accept in return for being assured that if you do survive, you will be entirely cured? (If a 10 percent risk, QOL is 0.9.)

Equivalence of Numbers How many more people with a given chronic, non-fatal illness would have to be saved from death to make saving their lives preferable to saving a smaller number of people in normal good health?[11] (If 10 percent more, QOL is 0.9.)

Direct Ratio How many times more ill is a person described in one specified state compared with another?[12]

If you turn out to be the paraplegic accident victim with 0.9 QOL and we could pursue a policy of producing more QALYs by saving someone else, to which of these questions would your answers that produced the 0.9 rating constitute consent to the policy that now lets you die?

Ambiguity plagues the direct ratio question. Where in 'how many times more ill..?' is it implied that very *lives* themselves, contrasted with death, are more and less worth saving? What is even meant by 'how many times more ill'?

The time trade-off question fares no better. In accepting a ten percent shorter remaining life to avoid a permanent disability, you do not indicate that quality adjusted trade-offs *between* different people's *very lives* are desirable.

Standard gamble suffers from a similar defect. With a 90 percent chance of complete cure from a certain treatment but also a 10 percent chance of dying, you are willing to use the treatment: you are directly expressing only what risks you will take *within your* life.

There is, however, an important conceptual connection between the willingness expressed in the standard gamble and the long-term use of QALYs. Endorsement of QALYs as an allocation method exposes you to a greater risk of being allowed to die should you ever be that paraplegic accident victim, but in return you gain a better chance of either receiving quality-enhancing treatment if you are a paraplegic or just being saved for prospectively normal health.[13] Let's call this *the QALY bargain*. It is not quite the same as the standard gamble, which concerns the risk of death you would accept to get a cure for your paraplegia. But if, knowing full well what a particular state of illness is like, one takes the gamble of a ten percent risk of dying in order to restore ourselves to good health, wouldn't one also take the QALY bargain?

Generally I think one would. Of course if one ever does get to the accident victim's situation and is paraplegic, one will probably want to live just as fervently as one would if one were the victim with prospective full health. But nonetheless, *if people think that, should they ever be in that situation, they would take the standard gamble, then why wouldn't they now be willing to look at their whole unfolding lives as a similar bargain*? That is, why wouldn't they take the QALY bargain, the risk of being allowed to die as a later paraplegic in order to have a greater chance of being saved for good health? Willingness to take a standard gamble does set some precedent for taking QALY bargains. Both pose explicit risk-of-death choices.

Better yet than standard gamble, though, would be 'equivalence of numbers,' where trade-offs between different people's lives are clear. And best of all would just be straightforward QALY-bargain questions themselves.[14]

Without some such explicit link between the questions used to establish quality indices and the use of QALYs to allocate resources, QALYs will persistently remain suspicious. But with those links in place the moral case for using quality of life adjustments begins to build. Then QOL-index responses indicate consent to competitive quality adjustment of one's own life, and QALY-counting methods begin at their very foundations to respect people's dignity and autonomy. If representative people have been asked true QALY-bargain questions in eliciting the QOL rankings, then we can presume that as later patients they have consented to the QALY-based benefit calculations that now leave them either beneficiary or victim of a rationing decision.

3. Quality-of-life improvements vs. lifesaving

Counting QALYs generates even more controversial implications than its lifesaving trade-offs. One of the more striking is that hip replacements, for example, which do not save lives at all, should probably take precedence over lifesaving haemodialysis.[15] It is not just hip replacements' relatively low expense that gives them their QALY edge.[16] Absolutely crucial are two other conceptual ingredients: estimating that hip replacements significantly improve QOL, and placing that improvement on the same scale as life itself.

Here we face a problem similar to the one we encountered in trading life for life. If I judge that hip replacements would improve life, say, from 0.9 to 1.0, I mean to say that they should be done before things that improve life less. But do I say anything at all about the comparison between such an improvement (lasting 20 years, e.g., for 2.00 QALYs) and saving someone's very life (of 0.90 quality for 2 years, say, for 1.80 QALYs)? Life itself looks so much different for people staring death in the face than quality enhancements usually look to people for whom less than life itself is at stake.[17]

The gap between peoples' values expressed in questionnaires and a policy of actually rationing by QOL might appear to be even greater here than it was in the life-for-life discussion. It probably isn't, however. For one thing, some quality improvements are immensely significant for people who need them. To say that life itself always looks more important to someone staring death in the face than quality enhancements look to someone with severe impairment is much too glib.

For another, some of the gap is closed by what people imply they are willing to risk. To be sure, with a time trade-off response they are only saying they would trade a longer time with worse health for a shorter time with better - no risk is involved. The standard gamble, however, speaks to risk. If one is willing to take such a gamble, can't we guess what risk one would also be willing to take regarding possible quality-enhancement/lifesaving trade-offs? To take this part of the QALY bargain, one has to risk turning out to be one of the kidney failure victims not saved with dialysis in return for the somewhat greater chance of getting a hip replaced if one should need that.[18] If someone is willing to take some standard gamble (a ten percent chance of dying, say, to have my hip fixed), wouldn't he or she also likely take this QALY bargain?

The standard gamble and QALY bargain are not, though, identical. Here, too, we ought to put the QALY bargain to respondents more directly than any standard gamble question does by itself.[19] The way to preserve respect for individual patients in QALY-maximizing policies is by getting the prior consent of the people those policies affect.

In this connection, a very important restriction on QALYs' use is revealed by the fact that their moral foundation is people's consent. One critic, O'Donnell, for example, throws the following rhetorical question up against QOL adjustment: 'What about the Dublin boy confined to a wheelchair since birth?'.[20] Should we really discount the value of saving his life because of its relatively low quality? Here (not elsewhere) O'Donnell is correct. There is no point in time at which such a boy can even be conceived or presumed to agree to any QALY bargains that make saving his life less urgent than saving the life of someone for normal health. The prior consent argument for QALYs does not apply to him or other cases of congenital impairments.

4. Whom should we question?

I have been pressing a query about consent: to just what have people really agreed when they gave answers to the various questions used to establish quality adjustment indices? This way of stating the query is admittedly, though, a bit misleading. Only a sample of people get questioned. Does this fact rob QALYs of their moral force?

To most of us, sampling itself is probably not very bothersome. To establish the initial QOL indices, it would be impossible to approach everyone who might be affected. If we have a good enough initial sample, therefore, is it not acceptable to presume the consent of people when only a few others have actually consented?[21]

The more important source of our moral doubts concerns whether we have asked the *right* sample. We could make the sample representative of the general population, but then we face a serious complaint: people who don't have these disabilities and illnesses may be more prepared than those who do to discount the value of living in worse health states. They do not know clearly how important life can be even to someone with impairment.

It is undoubtedly more difficult for healthy people to imagine accurately what they will think if they get a serious long-term impairment than it is for them to imagine what it will be like to face something like death that everyone commonly anticipates. So perhaps we should ask predominantly, or even exclusively, those who have had direct experience with the sorts of illnesses we are ranking.

There is also a more subtle argument for asking people who have had direct experience with the sort of illness in question. It starts with the same simple objection: people directly familiar with illness will rate the quality of their life in a given state of disability and distress as higher than others rate that sort of life. Suppose that the *difference* between highest and lowest QOL ratings by less healthy respondents is thus generally smaller than that difference in ratings by healthier respondents. What, though, does such a narrower difference mean? We are likely to forget that, within the QALY framework, it amounts to saying *two* things, not one, and that those two things pull in opposite directions: (1) Don't downgrade so much the priority of *saving* a given life just because it is impaired, but also (2) don't give as much weight to *remedying* that impairment.[22]

Saying both of those things leads to a real puzzle. Critics of QALYs complain that subjects without first-hand experience of lower quality life are biased, but in making that claim, *in which direction are the critics saying that subjects' rankings would shift if that bias were removed*? Within the conceptual framework that QALYs involve, we literally can't say. If people would quality-adjust things less, they would be giving those with impairments a smaller advantage than they otherwise would have in competing for quality-improving care. On the other hand, if they would quality-adjust their rankings more were they less biased, they would put people with impairments in a weaker position to compete for lifesaving measures. So how are less biased, more sympathetic-with-the-ill respondents supposed to respond?

There is only one way to regain conceptual order here. In charging that people without first-hand experience of impairment will be biased against the severely impaired and for those with normal health, critics must be claiming that people with experience of impairment rank both the remedying of impairments *and* the saving of lower quality lives more highly. But if they do both of those things, then they are in effect *rejecting the QALY framework itself*.

Perhaps, in fact, some respondents really want to reject it. And perhaps it is precisely this possibility that those designing the basic questions for constructing the quality index map are most apt to forget. After all, they are in 'the QALY business.' If knowledgeable participants just might express what amounts to a rejection of the quality adjustment framework itself, they should be given that chance via a sufficient variety of QALY-bargain questions. It is clearly not adequate to consult a good many people with experience of serious impairment if we do not ask the right questions.

We might wonder, though, whether this possibility of ranking both the QOL enhancement and the saving of lower quality lives more highly is coherent and not irrational. Suppose someone ranked improvement from paraplegia to normal health as fully half as important as saving the life of a person of normal health, but also ranked the saving of a paraplegic's life as equivalent in priority to saving the life of a normally healthy person. Is there anything defective about such a combination of preferences?

If we tried to squeeze this preference combination within the QALY framework, of course, it would amount to saying something very odd - (1) for quality enhancement purposes, paraplegia has a 0.5 QOL, while (2) at the same time, for lifesaving purposes, its QOL is 1.0. We have devised the QOL rating system precisely in order to put quality enhancement and lifesaving on the same scale, and yet here people are refusing to do precisely that. The question, however, is not whether this combination of preferences can be coherently squeezed into the QALY framework (it cannot), but whether the combination of preferences itself avoids irrationality. We would be begging the question if we argued that this combination is irrational *because* its QOL rankings cannot be coherently accommodated within the QALY framework.

So what about the combination itself? It does not deny that QOL enhancement can be compared to lifesaving - in the first preference, those are compared explicitly. It also does not deny that saving the life of a paraplegic can be compared with saving people for fully healthy lives--in the second preference, precisely those two are compared, and rated as equivalent. Presumably the person expressing both such preferences would also be thereby committed to saying that saving the life of a paraplegic had no more (and no less) than twice the weight of curing paraplegia.[23] Suppose a person of more normal health and less acquaintance with paraplegia would rank these differently--curing paraplegia, say, as 0.25 the weight of saving a normally healthy person, and saving the life of a paraplegic as 0.75 the value of saving a normal healthy person's life. That combination fits exactly into the unified QALY framework, but how is it itself any more rational than the former combination of preferences? I do not see that it is.

The proper conclusion has become clear. Indeed there appears to be a range of possible and not irrational lifesaving and impairment enhancing priorities that cannot be expressed in any single QOL comparison scale. If the moral argument for using QOL adjustment in a prioritization unit like QALYs rests on the claim that such adjustment can be presumed to represent the hard trade-off preferences of the very people QALYs are used to select in and out of selected health care, QALYs must somehow accommodate these 'odd' possibilities within their numerical QOL construction procedures. It might, of course, turn out that the real preferences of people with first-hand experience of illness and impairment can be perfectly well reflected in a QOL adjustment model, but it is important that actual coherent preferences, not the model, be the fundamental factor guiding our considerations.

In summary, we can see that undoubtedly much current resistance to QALYs simply misunderstands them, but not all of it does. QOL adjustment potentially reflects the way people rank their own lives, one of the strongest moral reasons for using QALYs in health policy. But without a base of more direct, QALY-bargain questions, and without some subtle and careful attention to whether people with experience of illness are rejecting the unitary QOL rating system itself, QALYs will continue to occupy a morally precarious position on the health policy stage.[24]

APPENDIX

Existing extrapolations of quality adjustment indices

Consulting patients and citizens to construct quality adjustment indices can be done in two ways. It can be direct: we question people with a particular condition to elicit their judgement about the relative quality of their own health status compared to being cured or dying. Or it can be more complicated and indirect: we first elicit a variety of persons' judgements about the quality of a whole spectrum ('map') of health states. From that data we extrapolate a numerical quality adjustment factor ('index') for each health status on the map, assuming that normal good health is 1.0 and death 0.0. Then, as a particular measure comes up for consideration later (e.g. kidney dialysis), we ask a sample of such patients various descriptive questions, using their responses to locate life with their treatment and condition on the previous map. Since a specific index of that location has been established by earlier respondents, we already have the quality adjustment factor for this particular condition.

Two notable studies concerning kidney patients' qualities of life have used the direct method. Asking CAPD[25] patients, chronic hemodialysis patients, and kidney transplant recipients what percentage shorter life with perfect health they would prefer over the likely longevity in their current condition, one study yielded quality adjustment scores of 0.57 for haemodialysis, 0.57 for CAPD, and 0.80 for transplantation.[26] Another study also revealed noticeably poor 'objective' quality of life for dialysis patients (work capacity, e.g.), but they gave much higher subjective ratings for their quality of life--roughly only 0.06 lower than the average QOL rating by the general population![27]

The indirect method has been used in Kind's, Rosser's, and Williams' work, utilized in some decisions in the British NHS.[28] For their initial map of health states Rosser and Kind combined four degrees of distress (none, mild, moderate, severe) with eight disability states:

1. No disability.
2. Slight disability.
3. Severe social disability or slight impairment at work.
   Able to do housework except for very heavy tasks.
4. Choice of work severely limited. Unable to do other than light housework, but able to go out shopping.
5. Unable to undertake any paid employment or continue any education. Confined to home if elderly.
6. Confined to chair or wheel chair, or able to move around in the home only with support of an assistant.
7. Confined to bed.
8. Unconscious.

Seventy subjects - general and psychiatric nurses, medical and psychiatric patients, healthy volunteers, and doctors - were asked to rank six particular combinations of disability and distress. They were asked, 'how many times more ill is a person in state x compared with state y?' Several assumptions were carefully explained, including the fact that their responses would carry two very important implications:

> a) The ratio you indicate between two states ['how many times more ill...'] will define the proportion of resources you would consider justifiable to allocate for the relief of someone in the more severe state compared with the less.
> b) The ratio will define your point of indifference between curing a number of the more ill people or some greater number of the less ill.[29]

Finally, subjects were asked to rank all the other 27 combinations of pain and disability and then to place the state of death somewhere on the scale of health states they had just ranked. The requisite interview of each subject lasted 1.5 to 4.5 hours!

Rosser and Kind converted their results to a scale where 1.0 is normal health (no disability, no distress) and 0.0 is death:

	Distress			
	A (none)	B (mild)	C (moderate)	D (severe)
Disability				
1. (none)	1.000	0.995	0.990	0.667
2. (slight)	0.990	0.986	0.973	0.932
3. ...	0.980	0.972	0.956	0.912
4. ...	0.964	0.956	0.942	0.870
5. ...	0.946	0.935	0.900	0.700
6. ...	0.875	0.845	0.680	0.000
7. (bed)	0.677	0.564	0.000	-1.486
8. (uncon.)	-1.028	---	---	---[30]

Respondents ranked states 6D and 7C (confined to chair and in severe distress, and confined to bed but in moderate distress) as equivalent to death. Of the states better than death, respondents ranked only three lower than 0.84--6C at 0.68, 7A at 0.677, and 7B at 0.564. All the others fell in the narrow range from 0.845 to 0.995.

Extrapolating such a map of quality adjustment indices, however, is only stage one. To assign an adjustment factor (index) to the particular state of a category of patient whose treatment is being evaluated, a second stage is necessary: elicit from such patients perceptions of where they fall in the disability/distress spectrum.

Overall the indirect, two-stage method seems preferable. Both the clarification of potentially confusing issues and the cross-checking of individuals' rankings of many different health states are indispensable if we are to reflect people's real quality-of-life estimates for tough trade-off decisions. The mind nearly boggles at the complexity of the questions and possible responses involved; as a practical matter, those are just too complex to be handled well directly with each category of patients who come up for priority assessment.

Obviously there are objectionable ways in which either direct or indirect method could be executed. Rosser and Kind constructed their original map from laudably detailed interviews with crucial clarifications, but their sample was small and contained certain unfortunate imbalances. Only six of the 70 participants were manual workers while 40 were professionals, and not even half had had experience with serious pain or illness.[31] This can be remedied.

Notes

1. Williams (1984, 1985b, 1986a) has been extremely explicit in putting the case for QALYs in terms of this ethical claim.
2. See Kaplan and Bush (1982) and Williams (1985a, 1986a). On hip replacements see Aaron and Schwartz (1984), p.92.
3. Smith (1985), p.23.
4. QOL adjustment might not actually be the most important part of QALYs; differences in the number of years of life saved in various categories of people are probably the weightier numerical factor. Few of the ratings on the Rosser-Kind scale fall below 0.845 (see Appendix). By contrast, the number of life years saved by competing procedures can easily vary by factors of five, ten, or more. I owe this observation to Roy Carr-Hill (University of York).
5. The 0.6 QOL rating is roughly that extrapolated by Churchill, Morgan, and Torrance (1984), pp. 21-22.
6. Saying hip replacements improve QOL from 0.9 to 1.0 is my own hypothesis. I base it on Rosser and Kind's disability/distress map, in which state 5C gets ranked 0.90 and state 1B 0.995. See Rosser and Kind (1978), p.349, and Kind, Rosser, and Williams (1982), p. 292. See Appendix for the breakdown of the disability/distress states they ranked.
7. See Appendix.
8. I am accepting the larger arguments here that any prior consent that people might give to general policies of rationing health care morally justifies the rationing later even when at that time it may disadvantage the person previously consenting. See Menzel (1990), chapters 1 and 2.
9. Harris (1986), p. 12.

10. Used, for instance, by Churchill, Morgan, and Torrance (1984).
11. Or how many people in a better state of illness would have to be cured for you to think the situation better than curing a smaller number of patients in a worse-off condition? Both questions are used by Rosser and Kind (1978), p. 350.
12. Used as the main question by Rosser and Kind (1978), p. 350. The term 'direct ratio' is mine; 'ratio scaling' is used by Torrance (1986), p. 25.
13. I do not expose myself to having *no* chance of being saved if I should ever turn out to be the victim with the prospect of 0.9 quality of life. The *cost per QALY* of saving me might still be less than the cost per QALY of saving someone else with higher life quality prospects. Because of this it is impossible to say just how much less is my chance of being saved as a 0.9 patient if QALYs become a primary allocation method. It cannot be said to be simply a ten percent smaller chance.
14. Rosser and Kind (1978) come remarkably close to such a QALY-bargain question despite their initial use of the rather weak direct ratio question. They laudably supplemented their main direct ratio question with both an equivalence question and the clarification that responses 'will define the proportion of resources...that you would consider it was justifiable to allocate for the relief of a person in the more severe state as compared with the less ill' (p. 350).
15. Williams (1985a).
16. $8000, to last 10-15 years, compared to dialysis at $30,000 per year.
17. If we refuse to say that some multiple of quality enhancements is preferable to saving one life, then lifesaving procedures like dialysis will likely get virtually absolute priority over quality improvements. John Harris (1986), p. 32, for example, concludes that 'only when *all* demands on resources for lifesaving have been met should life enhancement be undertaken' (emphasis added).
18. The bargain involved in QALYs is really more specific than this. Since use of QALYs attempts to maximize the QALYs we get for a given amount

of resources, we would be taking the risk of being the one person who doesn't get dialysis (saving $150,000, let us say, over five years), in return for having the chance of being one of the nearly 19 people who would have their hips replaced ($8000 per operation, for 10-15 years, each with 0.1 QOL improvement). Or if in fact there just aren't 19 people needing hip replacements to whom the resources saved from the dialysis could be shifted, ten might have their hips replaced and other people also helped with some procedure that was similarly cheaper per QALY than dialysis. In any case, in the QALY bargain my chances of being helped by something like a hip replacement are much greater than my chances of being left to die from kidney failure.

19. In this context equivalence-of-numbers questions do not help. They could, but not as usually stated. E.g., the clarification on the Rosser-Kind interviews (1978), p. 350, was that the preferences you express will define 'your point of indifference between curing one of the iller people or a [smaller] number...of the less ill people'. To get at the current issue the question would have to trade off one number of quality enhancements with another number of lives.
20. O'Donnell (1986). For a persuasive reply to other aspects of O'Donnell's attack on QALYs, see Williams (1986b).
21. To be sure, there are many important qustions about the moral relevance of presumed consent even beyond the matter of adequate representation. See Menzel (1990), chapter 2.
22. Remember the point made in section 1: while quality adjustment disadvantages impaired patients in competing for lifesaving measures, it benefits them in competition for quality enhancements.
23. If $A = 0.5 B$ and $B = C$, then $A = 0.5C$.
24. Much of this paper is based on Chapter 5 of Menzel (1990). The order and emphasis are different, and this paper's last section expands considerably on the discussion in the book.
25. Chronic ambulatory peritoneal dialysis.
26. Churchill, Morgan, and Torrance (1984), pp. 21-22. The value of normal health is 1.0; the value of death, 0.0.

27. In fact kidney *transplant* recipients rated their subjective quality of life *more* highly than the general population did theirs! See Evans, *et al.* (1985), pp. 556-57.
28. Rosser and Kind (1978), Kind, Rosser, and Williams (1982), and Williams (1981, 1985a). See also many applications by Gudex (1986).
29. Rosser and Kind (1978), pp. 349-350 (virtually but not precisely their phrasing).
30. Kind, Rosser, and Williams (1982), p. 160. States 8B, 8C, and 8D are considered void since an unconscious person would feel neither slight, moderate, nor severe distress.
31. Rosser and Kind (1978), p. 354. A considerably expanded and more balanced participant sample is currently being developed at the Centre for Health Economics, University of York.

6 Embryo experimentation and the moral status of the embryo

Peter Singer

Of all the issues raised by the new reproductive technology associated with *in vitro* fertilization, the most controversial continues to be that of the moral status of the embryo. This is the question at stake when we consider whether to create more embryos than we are willing to put back into the womb at one time; and it is also the issue involved in the debate over research on embryos.

One way of indicating the importance of moral status is to compare the differing ways in which we treat beings we regard as differing in moral status. In the United States a moratorium on the use of federal government funds for embryo experimentation has been in place for the past ten years.[1] Meanwhile the federal government continues to provide the funds for several million experiments on living, fully conscious animals every year.[2] In Britain, although the Warnock Committee recommended that experimentation on embryos should be allowed, this recommendation was hemmed in with restrictions: experiments to 14 days after fertilization only, and no large-scale production of embryos, for example for routine drug testing (as occurs with rats, mice, rabbits and other animals).[3] In my own state of Victoria, Australia, where the first legislation to regulate IVF and embryo experimentation was passed in 1984, there has been continued debate about embryo experimentation, and the legislation has already been amended in this area. At present the situation is that experimentation is allowed on 'surplus' or 'spare' embryos, but the fertilization of a human egg for research purposes is prohibited; in other words, embryos cannot be created specifically for research.[4] Animals, of course, are routinely created for research.

Why do scientists want to experiment on embryos? Research on the embryo offers the prospect of important medical advances. The first and most immediate prospect is in improving the success rate of *in vitro* fertilization. At present, IVF offers many infertile couples their best hope of a child; but it is still only a hope, with a success rate languishing in the region of 15-20% of egg collections resulting in a pregnancy. Since IVF is expensive, if there is no prospect of improving this success rate, it may be doubted if IVF is worth the resources now being allocated to it.

Scientists are also keen to do embryo research in order to ensure that embryos created from frozen human ova will develop normally, and to test techniques for micro-injection of sperm directly into the ovum, which may overcome male infertility due to low sperm count or abnormal sperm. The next area of research will be into the prevention of genetic defects. If defects can be identified in the early embryos, couples who carry defective genes and would otherwise seek testing during pregnancy, followed by abortion if the test is positive, will be able to use IVF, to be followed by the transfer only of those embryos which will not suffer from the defect. Further research may lead to the development of gene therapy, which could be effective in those cases where an individual has already been born with a single-gene defect like thalassaemia, sickle-cell anaemia, ADA and PNP deficiencies, and Lesch-Nyhan syndrome.[5]

The longer-term prospects are even more dramatic. On the strictly scientific front, they include, among many other possibilities, an enhanced understanding of the development of cancer cells, and quicker and more reliable methods of testing whether new drugs taken by pregnant women are likely to lead to deformed infants. The use of embryos could also provide an alternative to present methods of safety testing which involve considerable animal suffering. As far as clinical applications are concerned, the cultivation of blood stem cells could provide a cure for diseases such as sickle-cell anaemia and leukaemia; and eventually it may be possible to develop isolated organs which could be cultivated *in vitro* and used to replace diseased organs in children and adults.

Is such research acceptable? First, let me say that in this paper my focus is on the status of the embryo. I shall therefore not discuss the objection sometimes made that embryo experimentation poses a threat to women who may be subjected to hazardous medical treatments in order to make embryos available for scientists. The fact that I do not discuss this objection does not mean that I consider it unimportant, but only that it is a quite separate issue; indeed the crucial issue in that debate is not the moral status of the embryo, but the requirement of fully informed consent.[6]

To come then to the issue suggested by the title of my paper. The position I shall take is that once we free ourselves from a world view depending on some specifically religious premises, it is relatively straightforward to show that the early embryo does not have a right to life. To put the point in a preliminary way, which can serve as an initial rough approximation to the answer we shall reach: just as we regard brain *death* as the end of a person's life, so we should take brain *birth* as the start of a person's life. Before this time, therefore, we can use the embryo, with the consent of those from whose egg and sperm it has been formed, for scientific research.[7]

I shall not repeat in detail my reasons for taking this view, for I have stated them elsewhere. In essence, I think that the standard argument used by those who would attribute a right to life to the embryo is based on an equivocation. This argument is, of course, that every human being has a right to life, that the human embryo is a human being, and that therefore the human embryo has a right to life. The equivocation lies in the use of the term 'human being'. Undoubtedly the embryo is a human being in the sense of being a member of the species *Homo sapiens*, but is the embryo a human being in the morally relevant sense in which we think of human beings as having a special right of life which non-human animals, for instance, do not have? If we ask why humans should have some right to life over and above any right which may be possessed by dogs or pigs or marmosets, any plausible non-religious answer would have to seek the difference in our superior mental powers - our self-awareness, our rationality, our moral sense, our autonomy, or some combination of these. They are the kinds of thing, we are inclined to say, which make us truly human. To be more precise, they are the kinds of thing which make us *persons*. But if this is the sense in which we can agree that all human beings, or more strictly all persons, have a right to life, it is immediately clear that the embryo, especially the early embryo, is not a human being in this sense. The early embryo has no mental qualities which generally distinguish members of our species from members of other species. The early embryo has no brain, no nervous system. It is reasonable to assume that it has a mental life that is rather less interesting than that of an oyster. Or to put the matter with proper academic precision, it has no mental life at all.

It is still true that the human embryo is a member of the species *Homo sapiens*. That is, as we saw, why it is difficult to deny that the human embryo is a human being. But we can now see that this is not the sense of 'human being' we need to make the standard argument work. A valid argument cannot equivocate on the meanings of the central terms it uses. If the first premise is true when 'human' means 'a being with certain mental qualities' and the second premise is true when 'human' means 'member of the species *Homo sapiens*', the argument is based on a slide between the two meanings, and is invalid.

Can the argument be rescued? It obviously can't be rescued by claiming that the embryo is a being with the requisite mental qualities. That *might* be arguable for some later stage of the development of the embryo or fetus, but it is impossible to make out the claim for the early embryo. If the second premise cannot be reconciled with the first in this way, can the first perhaps be defended in a form which makes it compatible with the second? Can it be argued that human beings have a right to life, not because of any moral qualities they may possess, but because they - and not pigs, cows, dogs or lettuces - are members of the species *Homo sapiens*?

This is a desperate move. Those who make it find

themselves having to defend the claim that species membership is *in itself* morally relevant to the wrongness of killing a being. But why should species membership in itself be morally crucial? If we are considering whether it is wrong to destroy something, surely we must look at its actual characteristics, not just the species to which it belongs. If we were to encounter visitors from other planets who turn out to be sensitive, thinking, planning beings, would it be acceptable to kill them simply because they are not members of our species? Should you be in any doubt, ask yourself the same kind of question, but with 'race' substituted for 'species'. If we reject the claim that membership of a particular race is *in itself* morally relevant to the wrongness of killing a being, it is not easy to see how we could accept the same claim when based on species membership. Remember that the fact that other races, like our own, can feel, think and plan for the future is not relevant to this question, for we are considering membership of the particular group - whether race or species - as the sole basis for distinguishing between the wrongness of killing those who belong to *our* group, and those who are of some *other* group. As long as we keep this in mind, I am sure that we will conclude that neither race nor species can, in itself, provide any justifiable basis for such a distinction.

The argument from potential

At this point in the discussion, those who wish to defend the embryo's right to life often switch ground. We should not, they say, base our views of the status of the embryo on the mental qualities it *actually has while an embryo*; we must, rather, consider what it has the potential to *become*.[8]

In IVF, the egg and sperm are placed together in a glass dish, fertilization takes place, and the resulting embryo is transferred to the uterus. There is also a different procedure, known as GIFT (for gamete intrafallopian transfer) in which the eggs and sperm are obtained from the partners, and then - before fertilization - transferred into the fallopian tube, the place in the woman's body where fertilization normally occurs. In Melbourne, there is a Roman Catholic hospital which will not perform IVF, because it regards it as disrespectful of embryonic life, but will perform GIFT, because at no stage during the GIFT procedure is there an embryo outside the body. Instead there is an egg and some sperm, separated in the syringe used for the transfer by a bubble of air.

Consider the difference, in respect of potential, between the embryo formed in the course of the IVF procedure, prior to transfer to the uterus, and the gametes in the syringe prior to transfer to the fallopian tube during the GIFT procedure. In particular, suppose that in each situation, just as the syringe is loaded up for the transfer, the woman is discovered to have a medical condition which means that the transfer cannot take place. In these circumstances there are some who would say that to destroy the embryo would be gravely wrong, but to destroy the egg and sperm, separated by their bubble of air, would not be wrong at all, or would be much less seriously wrong. In terms of preventing a possible person from existing, however, there is no difference at all (or if there is, it depends on the success rate of one procedure rather than the other; and in fact GIFT has the higher success rate, so if anything the destruction of the gametes comes closer to preventing a possible person existing than the destruction of the embryo). So it cannot be preventing the existence of a possible future person that makes it wrong to dispose of the embryo, but not of the gametes.

If this example appears to have failed to capture some sense of potential relevant to the embryo which would explain the difference between the embryo in itself, and the egg and sperm, it would be good if those defending this difference could offer a clear account of what this difference is. I suspect that the problem is this. The argument from potential derives, not from the debate over embryo experimentation or IVF, but from the abortion debate. In that context, it is possible to say of the embryo from the moment of conception that there is a *natural* course of events which, in the absence of accident or deliberate interference, means that a child will result. Even in the case of the *in vivo* situation, this is not entirely true; there is evidence to suggest that in normal sexual reproduction, a majority of conceptions fail to implant, and are unnoticed, early miscarriages,[8] but certainly it is true that by the time a pregnancy is sufficiently established to be noticeable, it has a better than 50% chance of resulting in a child, if there is no deliberate interference. In contrast, eggs and sperm do not unite and grow into a child without some deliberate human acts (deliberate in one sense, anyway, even if not deliberate in respect of an intention to produce a child).

If I am right about this being the basis for the argument from potential, however, it is clear that it cannot easily be transferred from the abortion debate to the IVF and embryo experimentation debate. For in the laboratory the contrast between the embryo and the gametes breaks down. Now both the egg and sperm, when they are separate, *and* the embryo need human assistance if they are to develop further. Since the probabilities of this development succeeding are not all that different, I cannot see how there can be a sharp difference in their potential.

In defence of the argument from potential, it might be said that even though an egg and a drop of seminal fluid have the potential to lead to a future human person, the potential is at this stage indeterminate, because it is not known which sperm will fertilise the egg. Thus there is as yet no genetically unique human individual. Once the embryo exists, there is. This is of course correct, although its relevance is unclear. The potential of the egg and collection of sperm is to become a future human person, and, with rare exceptions, every human person is genetically unique. Why does it matter that *at this stage* the particular genetic constitution of the individual is still to be determined?

I have not seen a satisfactory answer to this question. But suppose such an answer were available; new technology poses new problems for the argument from genetic determinacy. The technique I have in mind involves fertilizing an egg by micro-injection, using a single sperm. It is being developed to overcome a form of male infertility that results from the male having too few, or insufficiently motile, sperm.[9] When this technique is perfected, the genetic constitution of the future person will be determined when the egg and sperm have been selected. Will this then be the moment at which moral status changes? Somehow I doubt that this is what those who wish to protect the embryo will say; but the new technique will knock out one more ground for holding that the status of the embryo is markedly different from that of the egg and sperm, when separate but considered jointly.

It may still be said that the embryo is an *individual*, whereas the egg and sperm are not, and hence the embryo is a being with the potential to become a person, whereas the egg and sperm, when still separate, are not a single entity at all. Two distinct points need to be made about this claim. First, we need to keep in mind that we are here focussing on the argument from potential. We have already seen that the fact that this single entity is of the species *Homo sapiens* is not in itself a reason for saying that it is more worthy of protection than a single entity of any other species would be. In pointing to the fact that the embryo is a single entity, there is a temptation to slide back into that argument. If, however, the claim is that it is not because of the species of this single entity that it is worthy of special protection, but because of what this single entity of the species *Homo sapiens* may become, then we are looking ahead, and it seems no less appropriate to look at what may become of two separate entities, if we put them together and transfer the result to a woman's uterus, than it does to look at what will become of a single entity, if we transfer it to a woman's uterus.

The second point to make about the claim that the embryo is an individual is that this may not be an accurate description of the early embryo, which consists of, say, 8 cells. At this stage, each cell has the potential to develop into a separate individual; and this sometimes happens, when identical twins are formed. If the embryo was an individual human being before that point, what happens to that individual when twins form? Does the pre-existing individual become just one of the twins? But which one? Or does the pre-existing individual die? Strange death, that leaves no corpse! If it is an individual human being we are seeking, we might do better to postpone making any claims for the embryo until the possibility of twin formation is past. This can be taken to be about 14 days after fertilization, so it provides some kind of basis for the recommendation, made for example by the Warnock Committee, that embryo experimentation should be permitted only up to this time.[10] As I have said, however, I do not think that the moment when an individual of the species *Homo sapiens* comes into existence is really morally important. Instead, I shall sketch an alternative account.

A positive approach

We have now seen the inadequacy of the most popular attempts to argue that the early embryo has a moral status superior to that of nonhuman animals, and is hence worthy of much greater protection. Although there are other arguments for this view, it is not possible in the space available to consider them all. It remains only to say something positive about when in its development the embryo may acquire rights.

The answer must depend on the actual characteristics of the embryo. Earlier I suggested that, by analogy with the widespread acceptance of the idea that people are dead when their brains have irreversibly ceased to function, we might consider that people are first 'alive', in the sense relevant to the attribution of moral status, when their brains first begin to function. But this is only an approximation. Brain death is an event; the birth of the brain is a gradual process. What we should really be looking for are the morally significant mental developments, which of course will require a functioning brain, but are not to be identified with brain function itself.

The minimal characteristic which is needed to give the embryo a claim to consideration is sentience, or the capacity to feel pain or pleasure. Until the embryo reaches that point, there is nothing we can do to the embryo which causes harm to *it*. We can, of course, damage it in such a way as to cause harm to the sentient being it will become, if it lives, but if it never becomes a sentient being, the embryo has not been harmed, because its total lack of awareness throughout its life means that it never has had any interests at all.

In sharp contrast to the embryo at this early stage of its existence, non-human animals such as monkeys, dogs, rabbits, guinea pigs, rats and mice clearly can feel pain, and thus often are harmed by what is done to them in the course of scientific research. I have already suggested that the species of a being is not, in itself, relevant to its ethical status. Why then is it considered acceptable to poison conscious rabbits in order to test the safety of drugs and household chemicals, but not considered acceptable to carry out tests on totally non-sentient embryos? It is only when an embryo reaches the stage at which it may be capable of feeling pain that we need to control the experimentation which can be done with it. At this point the embryo ranks, morally, with those non-human animals I have mentioned. These animals have often been unjustifiably made to suffer in scientific research. We should have stringent controls over research to ensure that this cannot happen to embryos, just as we should have stringent controls to ensure that it cannot happen to animals.

At what point does the embryo develop a capacity to feel pain? Though I am not an expert in this field, from my reading of the literature, I would say that it cannot possibly be earlier than six weeks, and it may well be as late as eighteen or twenty weeks.[11] So while I think we should err on the side of caution, it seems to me that the 14 day limit suggested by the Warnock committees is *too* conservative. There is no doubt that the embryo is not sentient for some time after this date. Even if we were to be very, very cautious in erring on the safe side, a 28 day limit would provide sufficient protection against the possibility of an embryo suffering during experimentation. I have already said that there may be other objections to embryo experimentation, particularly regarding the autonomy of the woman from whom the eggs are collected. But if it can be shown that embryos are obtainable in unobjectionable ways, embryo experimentation should be permitted, up to 28 days after fertilization.

Notes

1. Office of Technology Assessment (1988), pp. 178f.
2. For details see my (1989), ch. 2.
3. Warnock Committee (1984), paras. 11.22, 12.5.

4. Parliament of Victoria, *Infertility (Medical Procedures) Act, 1984*; *Infertility (Medical Procedures) (Amendment) Act, 1987.*
5. For details see Trounson (1990).
6. See Warren (1990).
7. In saying this I echo the view defended by Lockwood, in his (1988); but my reasons for reaching this conclusion differ from Lockwood's, as will become clear later in this essay.
8. See the paper by Matti Hayry, 'Infanticide on request - the dark side of liberal abortion policies', in this volume.
9. Roberts and Lowe, (1975); Muller *et al*, (1980).
10. Trounson, *op. cit.*
11. See Ford (1989); and Kuhse and Singer (1990).
12. See Grobstein (1988), pp. 54-55.

7 Infanticide on request: The dark side of liberal abortion policies?

Matti Hayry

Liberal abortion policies are often theoretically based on the premise that fetuses are not persons, that is, people in the ethically relevant sense, and that it is therefore not seriously wrong to kill them. The opponents of these policies have noted, however, that the definitions given to the concept of a 'person' are usually so demanding that new-born infants, as well as fetuses, fail to fulfil the necessary conditions. And although abortion may be generally accepted in many modern Western countries, infanticide, in turn, is often regarded as totally damnable - killing an innocent child is, for many people, the paradigmatic case of doing evil. Thus, the mere possibility of infanticide seems to constitute a strong argument against liberal abortion policies.

In present-day reality, the problem is in many countries further exacerbated by the availability of high-tech neonatal care along with a legal right to terminate pregnancies even at their latest stages. It is in certain cases possible that a fetus about to be aborted is already viable - that unless it is deliberately killed during the termination, it would be capable of living as a separate human being in the outside world. Abortion in these cases seems in many respects to come close to infanticide in the proper sense.

My aim in the present study is to describe systematically the emergence of the argument from infanticide in the abortion issue, and to examine how the defenders of liberal abortion policies might respond to it without committing themselves to clearly unacceptable practices. I shall take as my starting point for discussion the conservative, or 'Catholic', argument, and the problems of personhood and (especially) potentiality that arise thereby. In what follows, the thrust of the argument will then be turned against the liberal view, and in the rest of the paper a defence of the liberal position is reconstructed by adding to the premises of the discussion the moral weight of women - as opposed to the weight of fetuses and infants.

The point of departure: the Catholic argument

There are three major approaches to the morality of abortion and related issues: the *restrictive* view, stating that abortion (and perhaps also the use of contraceptives) should be abandoned altogether; the *moderate* view, stating that while some steps may be taken to control human reproduction, the measures employed should not be too radical; and the *liberal* view, according to which there are no good grounds for rejecting either abortion or - within certain limits, at least - infanticide.

All restrictive abortion policies are nowadays directly or indirectly based on the alleged human rights of the fetus. It is supposed, in the arguments for these policies, that fetuses have a right to life, and that they should not be killed during the pregnancy. Sometimes a different vocabulary is employed, and opponents of liberal and moderate abortion policies refer to our duties to respect and abstain from harming unborn human life. But for as long as the practical imperative implied by the language of duties remains exactly the same as that implied by the language of rights - fetuses should never be killed - I presume that what can be said for and against fetal rights can also be applied to duties toward and respect for fetal human life.

There are, however, some qualifications that are usually added to the premises so as to make them consistent with justifiable self-defence, and justifiable warfare. With these additions, the complete presentation of an argument for restrictive abortion policies takes the following form:

(P1) Every innocent human being has a right to life.
(P2) Fetuses are innocent human beings.
(C1) Therefore, fetuses have a right to life.
(P3) No being which has a right to life should be directly killed.
(C2) Therefore, fetuses should not be directly killed.
(P4) Fetuses are directly killed in abortions.
(C3) Therefore, abortions should not be performed.

I have used the name *Catholic argument* to refer to this construction.[1]

There are two critical points here, which have been picked up by the argument's detractors. Firstly, the meaning of the phrase 'human being' may well differ in premises P1 and P2. If that is the case, then the rest of the argument collapses, and the way is wide open for liberal abortion policies. And secondly, premise P3 is not necessarily true, either. Counterexamples have been given to show that it is not always wrong to kill (directly) a being possessing a right to life. Even if the first conclusion C1 holds, then, the falsity of P3 perhaps accommodates moderate policies at least.

The latter objection has been developed, for instance, by Philippa Foot and Judith Jarvis Thomson.[2] I shall not go into details here, but what Foot's and Thomson's contributions to the debate show is that premise P3 of the Catholic argument is, if not plainly false, then at least very probably inapplicable to the abortion issue. It is not always wrong to kill a fetus even if it does have a right to life. This is because sometimes even the very basic rights of individual human beings are in conflict with each other, and in such cases one is normally under no obligation to sacrifice one's own good for the good of others or, worse still, for the sake of a rigid moral system. In short, if the pregnant woman is considered to be a human being worthy of the same protection the fetus is entitled to within the Catholic argument, then conflicting rights make the decision to abort, in some circumstances at least, much more difficult to assess than the proponents of the argument would like to think.

Personhood and its importance

However, there are strict limits to the application of these results if it is presumed that conclusion C1 of the Catholic argument is valid. The main difficulty with any argument based on conflicting rights in this context is that it does not really establish the justification for killing the fetus save in some special circumstances. It may sometimes be appropriate to defend oneself even at the cost of causing the death of another human being, and this enables one to permit abortions in situations where the continuation of the pregnancy would pose a serious threat to the woman's life. But when the fetus is regarded as another human being with equal rights, this is as far as one can go along with moderate and liberal policies.

But all this is true only if fetuses have a right to life. And that, in turn, is the case only if premises P1 and P2 of the Catholic argument are mutually compatible, that is, if fetuses are human beings in the ethically relevant sense that furnishes people with rights, among them the right to life. Let me call, following the trend in contemporary discussion, beings in this 'ethically relevant sense' *persons*.

There are several suggestions as to who or what is a person, but I shall, for argument's sake, ignore the more moderate definitions in favour of a radical view concerning the matter, stated by Michael Tooley in 1972:

> An organism possesses a serious right to life only if it possesses the concept of a self as a continuing subject of experiences and other mental states, and believes that it is itself such a continuing entity.[3]

The point of Tooley's position can be put as follows.[4] That a being has a right to life implies that by killing the being one would, in most cases, violate this right. But not always, since, say, an adult human being may, in some circumstances, genuinely wish to die, and in circumstances like that it is not possible to violate her or his right to life. One can violate a being's right to life only if that being *wants* to live. And only entities possessing and being aware of possessing the concept of a self as a continuing subject of mental states are capable of wanting to live. Therefore, only such entities are capable of having a right to life.

Assuming that Tooley's account of persons and rights is correct, the opponents of liberal abortion policies seem to be in trouble. Fetuses do not, at any stage of their development, possess the concept of a self – or any other concept, for that matter – and thus they fail to fulfil the necessary conditions of personhood. The first and second premises of the Catholic argument have to be reformulated to say, for instance:

(P1') Every innocent person has a right to life.
(P2') Fetuses are innocent members of the species *homo sapiens*.

From these premises nothing follows, and with the invalidity of conclusion C1 the whole argument collapses.

The non-importance of potential personhood

There is, however, a line of argument the opponents of liberal policies can use in order to defend their original position. Fetuses are not persons, they admit, but as members of the species *homo sapiens* they will, in time, *become* persons if nobody interferes with their natural development. They are not actual persons, but they are potential persons, and as such they possess a right to life.[5] The early steps of the Catholic argument can now be written in the following form:

(P1") Every potential person has a right to life.
(P2") Fetuses are potential persons.
(C1) Therefore, fetuses have a right to life.

And as the reformulation reinstates conclusion C1, the grounds are once again firm for building moderate or restrictive abortion policies.

With the introduction of *potentiality* one of the most critical points of the contemporary abortion discussion is reached. The difficulty with the argument based on the potential personhood of the fetus is that its main premise P1" seems to come more or less out of nowhere. Apart from some Christian declarations[6] and some quasi-philosophical reflections on the issue,[7] no real arguments have been presented in favour of the view that every potential person has a right to life. The best I can do, therefore, is to bring up some possible arguments for the view, and see how these have been refuted in recent literature.

The first possibility is to argue that there is a general rule saying that *all potential beings of a given kind possess all the ethical characteristics of actual beings of the same kind*. And as actual persons have a right to life, the same must be true with regard to potential persons. But no such general rule exists: there are two neat counterexamples in the literature. Peter Singer has pointed out that while Charles, the Prince of Wales, is a potential king of England, he does not at the moment possess the rights of a king.[8] And John Harris has noted that while all living human beings are potentially dead human beings, it does not follow that they should be treated as dead before they actually die.[9]

The second possibility is to *argue that all human potentialities must be actualized, in the sense that it would be wrong to prevent or not to bring about the actualization of all potential human beings*. The problem with this view is that it requires, in practice, much more than most reasonable people would be ready to accept. If it is our duty to actualize all potential human beings, then we also have to condemn, along with abortion and contraception, celibacy and any kind of control over procreation. All fertile women should be pregnant all the time, and no effort should be saved in research to find ways of cloning people directly from ordinary human cells.[10] In fact, according to this view it would be our duty to overpopulate the world to a greater extent than at present, eventually dying of hunger and disease when our planet cannot support us any more. In this way, then, actualizing all potential human beings today could, in fact, kill the whole of mankind tomorrow.

The third possibility is to suggest that *there is, in some sense, a person inside of each and every fetus or embryo or zygote right from the moment of conception*. Accordingly, it is not the disposing of the fetus that is so wrong with abortion, it is the destroying of the person inside the fetus. This argument is, of course, false because there is no person inside the unborn human being. But it is most probable that this is the line of argument many people have in mind when they defend the rights of the unborn. Robert M. Gordon has lucidly analyzed this kind of thinking in his article 'The Abortion Issues'.[11] As he points out, people seem to think that there is a Beethoven or an Einstein or at least a John or Joan Smith hidden in every fetus, like the handsome prince who was hidden in the enchanted frog in the fairy tales. It is only after one consciously rids oneself of this idea that one can see the potential personhood of the fetus in a rational way. The fetus is not a person, but, if certain conditions prevail, it will in time become a person. On the other hand, if the fetus is aborted, that person will never come into being. And we owe no duties towards persons who never existed or will never exist.

The fourth possibility is to attempt to save, at another level, the foregoing argument. *Although there is, in fact, no person in the fetus, we can imagine that there is*. And if we asked this imaginary person whether she wanted to live, the answer would obviously be in the affirmative. We can verify this fact by imagining ourselves in the position of the person in the fetus: clearly we would want to live, if we were in her place. And since abortion, if performed on us during our fetal time, would have violated our present right to life, abortion performed on a fetus now would also violate the right to life of the person the fetus will become.[12]

This line of argument contains at least one major flaw. As Richard Brandt has noted in his article 'The Morality of Abortion', there is no reason to believe that the imaginary person in the fetus would even want the future actual person to live, even if it were given the choice to decide about the matter. Brandt presents the following example to elucidate the point:

> Suppose I were seriously ill, and were told that, for a sizeable fee, an operation to save 'my life' could be performed, of the following sort: my brain would be removed to another body which could provide a normal life, but the unfortunate result of the operation would be

> that my memory and learned abilities would be wholly erased, and that the forming of memory brain traces must begin again from scratch, as in a newborn baby. Now, how large a fee would I be willing to pay for this operation, when the alternative is my peaceful demise? My answer would be: none at all.[13]

The point of Brandt's example is that memory is an important factor in the continuity of a person's existence. If the object of Brandt's operation would lose all memories, he would have no objective reason to want some other person to live with his brain in the future. And this is exactly the situation the imaginary person in the fetus finds herself in. Nobody has any memories from one's own fetal time, and so the imaginary person is in no way connected to the future person. Therefore, the imaginary person has no subjective reason to want the future person to live.

The fifth, and last, possibility to defend the potentiality thesis is to say that, apart from any exterior reasons or grounds, *it is just another fact of life that potential personhood guarantees to its bearer the same right to life as actual personhood does*. Let me show how Michael Tooley has formulated and refuted this view. He writes:

> The [defence of restrictive and moderate abortion policies] will rest upon the following two claims: first, that there is a property, even if one is unable to specify what it is, that (i) is possessed by adult humans, and (ii) endows any organism possessing it with a serious right to life. Second, that if there are properties which satisfy (i) and (ii) above, at least one of those properties will be such that any organism potentially possessing that property has a serious right to life even now, simply by virtue of that potentiality, where an organism possesses a property potentially if it will come to have that property in the normal course of its development.[14]

But this *potentiality principle*, as Tooley calls it, cannot be defended. Opponents of liberal abortion policies use it to prohibit acts (and only acts) preventing fetuses from becoming adult human beings. It is, however, from the moral point of view, indifferent whether the undesirable result is caused by acting in a certain way or omitting to act in another way, provided that there are no additional differences between the two. Thus, if it is seriously wrong to prevent, by performing abortions, new life from actualizing, it is also seriously wrong to abstain from creating new life whenever it is possible. So this argument turns out to be just another version of the actualizing all potential human beings argument, which has already been refuted.[15]

Gametes vs. fetuses: separateness and improbability[16]

However, the refutation of both the second and last interpretations above is based on the assumption that any separate female-male pair of human gametes is as much of a potential person as an embryo after conception, or a more developed fetus or a newborn infant. Against this, an opponent of the liberal view can argue that there are at least two points of distinction which may be relevant and, if so, undermine the refutation. First, after conception the individual constitutes a oneness, whereas the gametes are separate from each other: it can be argued against the potentiality of the egg and the sperm, as opposed to that of the embryo, that it does not make sense to talk about the common potentiality of two discrete and mutually independent beings. And second, the probability of an embryo or a fetus becoming a person is far greater than that of two randomly selected separate gametes: consequently, if one destroys a developed fetus, one may well act more immorally than if one destroys a spermatozoon.

Peter Singer and Karen Dawson have answered the first part of this challenge by a direct counterattack:

> [T]here is no reason why an entity with potential must consist of a single object, rather than of two or more discrete objects. There is, for instance, nothing problematic about the statement (made, let us assume, shortly before the battle of El Alamein) 'Montgomery's army has the potential to defeat Rommel's army.' Yet Montgomery's army consisted

> of thousands of discrete individuals, spread over many miles of desert. We can even speak of the potential of entities which are spread across the entire planet - as Noah might have spoken of the potential of the raindrops falling all over the world to cause a great flood. So why should there be any problem about speaking of the potential of a set of gametes in a glass dish?[17]

It is not entirely clear whether this response is satisfying as such. It is true, of course, that the soldiers of Montgomery's army and the raindrops forming the flood were separate entities, which jointly achieved something any one of them could not have achieved without the others. But there seems to be something more to the fusion of the gametes than mere 'quantity becoming quality', as in Montgomery's and Noah's cases. The sperm and the egg in themselves carry the genetic inheritance of only one would-be parent, whereas after conception the embryo is a genetic combination of both of the parents, and has irreversibly become a new individual. What is important here is the *irreversibility* of the process - after the battle, the army became reduced into individuals again, after the flood, the raindrops became reduced to separate drops of water again, but the embryo does not and cannot become a pair of gametes any more. And this difference *could* have relevance in the potentiality issue.

The argument presented by Singer and Dawson can, however, be saved by employing a slightly different example. Consider a potential painting, which at the moment physically consists of a piece of cloth waiting in the atelier, and a set of oil colours on the counter of an artists' shop. Consider, further, that the painter is just about to step into the shop to buy the set, after which she will go to the atelier and paint the picture she has composed in her head for weeks. It seems clear that the colours and the cloth in this situation have the potential of becoming a painting, although they are separate in the same manner as the egg and the sperm are before conception. And since the artistic process is irreversible in the sense that the aesthetic qualities of the painting, once the work is completed, cannot be reduced to mere oil and cloth any more, the possible objection in the Montgomery and Noah cases is evaded. Separateness indeed seems to be no obstacle to the possession of potential.

What proponents of the potentiality view could state, at this point, is that the artistic example fails to support my refutations since it strongly limits the scope of separate entities possessing common potentialities. The way the situation is described, the only pairs of gametes to analogously have the potential of becoming persons are those waiting in the laboratory to be unified by *in vitro* fertilization (IVF). And what is more, the IVF process in question should exceptionally occur between only one sperm and one egg to make the analogy tight enough to justify the comparison. Thus, even if one admits that the analogy holds in these cases, the admission would hardly imply an obligation to overpopulate the world in the name of saving all identifiable potential human beings.

There is a hidden premise in the critique, namely that the probability of the relevant outcome is a factor in considering whether or not given entities possess morally important potentialities. For instance, a developed fetus not facing the prospect of termination has a very high probability of becoming a person, as compared to a random pair of gametes, and this is considered ethically important according to the critique. But the premise is not in fact true - an example illustrates the point. Suppose that there are ten newborn babies in the maternity ward of a city hospital, all healthy but ranging socio-economically from millionaires' children to the children of the least well-off groups within society. Now, although the chances of the millionaire infant to live to be a person in Tooley's sense are presumably better than the like chances of the poorest child at the ward, this cannot have the ethical implication that one has a stronger right to life than the other.

The challenge from infanticide

It seems, then, that despite the many lines of argument which can be evoked in favour of the importance of potential personhood in the abortion debate, no good grounds can ultimately be found for thinking that potential as well as actual persons possess a right to life. But granted this, the problem presented in the beginning of the paper now arises. If only actual persons have a right to life, and if only entities possessing and being aware of possessing the concept of a self as a continuing subject of mental states are persons, then newborn babies as well as fetuses lack personhood, and, along with it, the right to life. However, even those who accept abortion on any grounds usually reject infanticide. Therefore, liberal abortion policies seem to face a dilemma here: either abortion is accepted because of the non-personhood of fetuses, in which case the possibility of infanticide works as a *reductio ad absurdum* of the morality of these policies; or it must be admitted that newborn infants have a right to life, in which case the fetuses, too, must have a right to life, and the liberal theory collapses.

Severely handicapped infants: the Kuhse-Singer theory

It is ordinarily assumed within the liberal camp that the morality of infanticide varies along with the physical condition of the newborn infant. Basically, there are two kinds of situation, each requiring sharply different responses. Firstly, if the neonate seems to be capable of developing into a full person with fears, hopes and the ability to make judgements concerning the value of his own life, then infanticide should always be forbidden. No one else can legitimately make decisions like this on behalf of a separate individual human being who will, in the course of time, become capable of making such decisions for himself - indeed to do so would even, according to popular liberal thinking, amount to deliberate murder. Secondly, if the child is so severely handicapped that one cannot reasonably expect it to become a person at all, then the situation is different, and the general criteria of non-voluntary euthanasia can be employed. A hedonistic calculation should be made, weighing up the pleasures and pains the child is expected to enjoy or suffer during his lifetime. If the result is strongly negative, that is, if there is thought to be overwhelming suffering and little if any enjoyment or pleasure, infanticide should be considered our duty, just as it is the usual practice when animals are suffering. If the result is positive or indifferent, then keeping or not keeping these children alive will be largely a question of resources and attitudes.

In their book *Should the Baby Live?*, Helga Kuhse and Peter Singer present a solution to the problem of infanticide as far as seriously damaged babies are concerned: their proposition is that the parents of severely handicapped infants should be left with a choice as to whether or not to keep the baby alive.[18] During the first few weeks of the infant's life it would be up to the parents to decide whether the family can take care of the child or not, and whether the child, according to their judgement, will ever have a life worth living. If and only if both the answers to these questions are negative, then to kill or let the newborn die should, according to Kuhse and Singer, be normally permitted by law. An exception to the rule is that if the assessment of outside observers would drastically differ from that of the parents, i.e. if it seems to them apparent that the child would, in fact, have a worthwhile life in spite of the parents' judgement to the contrary, then it would be justifiable for the state to interfere and keep the baby alive either by placing her in an institution or by giving her to adoptive parents who are willing and able to take good care of her. Within this model it would be possible to let hopeless cases die, or even actively to help them die, while maintaining that no child with a positive life expectancy should be neglected.

If the cases referred to by Kuhse and Singer concern newborn infants which altogether lack the capacity of becoming persons, their suggestion may well be considered acceptable in moderate as well as liberal circles: it would be patently inhumane to keep alive seriously defective and suffering infants who, during the months or years they live, do not develop any kind of consciousness of themselves or of their surroundings.[19] And it would perhaps also be inhumane to force the parents to face these depressing months or years.

But granted that infanticide may be justifiable as regards defective babies with no prospects of personhood, the real challenge of infanticide against liberal abortion policies still remains: the challenge of making a moral distinction between killing *healthy* babies and aborting *healthy* fetuses. Neither fetuses nor newborn infants are persons, and if one wishes to protect the latter group in the spirit expressed above while leaving the former group unprotected, one must be prepared to point out the morally relevant factor that separates the classes from each other. Especially in the case of viable fetuses the problem is acute: embryos and early fetuses lack many important features such as sentience, human form and the capability of surviving independently, but about the only feature that separates a viable fetus, as such, from the newborn baby is that the latter is breathing by means of her own pair of lungs. Abortion on request at the late stages of the pregnancy seems to imply infanticide on request, and if one wants to condemn this possibility, then a firm dividing line should be stipulated.

The relevance of birth?

Up to this point, only gametes, fetuses, babies and a neutral class of sexless parents have been mentioned with any degree of seriousness in the argument - there has been little or no reference made to the women who bear the fetuses and whose lives are also at issue in decisions concerning abortion. Once *their* existence and wishes are taken into account as well, the picture may start changing quite considerably. An obvious difference between the fetus and the baby is, namely, that the former is inside the woman, the latter is not. The difference is 'extrinsic' in the sense that the right to live of the beginning human life is not changed thereby - but there are at least two factors which may be considered relevant to an ethical assessment.

Firstly, as Mary Ann Warren has noted, birth marks a dividing line in *attitudes* towards the fetus:

> [M]ost people care deeply about infants, particularly (but not exclusively) their own. The infant at birth enters the human social world, where (if it lives) it becomes involved in social relationships with other human beings, of a kind that can only be dimly foreshadowed before birth. It begins to be known and cared for, not just as a *potential* new member of the family or community, but as a socially present and responsive individual.[20]

Warren goes on to attribute the caring attitude toward infants to the influence of laws, which often treat 'live birth as the point at which a legal person comes into existence'.[21] That birth is significant is, then, originally a legal fiction, but as such a very convenient one.

Secondly, birth is also important from the viewpoint of individual *autonomy*. Kuhse and Singer write about this aspect of the matter:

> Unlike the foetus, the new-born infant can be cared for by others without compelling the mother to continue a pregnancy which will result in a baby she does not want. Respect for a woman's sovereignty over her own body requires us to allow women to choose an abortion. [...] We can allow women - and men - maximum sovereignty over their bodies, and still deny them the right to insist on the deaths of their children.[22]

If Kuhse and Singer are correct, respect for the privacy and autonomy of women - and of adult human beings in general - permits the morally relevant distinction to be made between the treatment of fetuses on one hand and of infants on the other. Thus, if social facts and privacy are relevant to the abortion and infanticide issue, it seems that birth does mark a dividing line between the morality of abortion and the immorality of infanticide. Unfortunately, however, the relevance is not as clear as one might wish to think.

One problem with Warren's view is that in referring to the alleged facts concerning people's attitudes she does not provide any empirical or conceptual evidence for their validity. Yet it is perfectly feasible that people either care as much about fetuses (their own 'unborn children') as they do about infants, or as little about both. Another problem is that even if people did feel more warmly about children than about fetuses, this in itself does not prove that there is a morally relevant distinction between them. Many people like members of their own racial group better than those of other racial groups, but this does not prove the existence of an ethically significant difference. Why should prevailing attitudes be more important in the abortion and infanticide issue?

Kuhse and Singer, too, despite their apparent emphasis on feminine autonomy, go on to qualify their view in a manner that refutes the original interpretation:

> [Only] if abortion is equivalent to the death of the foetus, then - since the foetus has no intrinsic right to life - respect for a woman's sovereignty over her own body requires us to allow women to kill their foetuses. Once the foetus can survive outside the woman's body, however, the connection between the woman's right to choose and the death of the foetus disappears.[23]

Notice the expression 'once the fetus *can survive* outside the woman's body' - instead of, say, 'once the fetus *is* outside the woman's body' - which guarantees every (healthy and) viable fetus the same protection against violence as has already been granted to (healthy) infants. In other words, Kuhse and Singer annul the woman's right to privacy and sovereignty over her body the moment the fetus becomes viable. From the liberal point of view, such an annulment is extremely dangerous: it is, for instance, consistent with the American conservative plans to allow the screening of fetuses for viability, and, where viability is detected, to deny abortions and subject women to various unpleasant and risky prenatal procedures. Respect for the life of the fetus could require physicians to force women in labour to undergo caesarean sections against their own will, and many kinds of *in utero* surgery which may benefit the fetus but inflict harm on the woman ought to be performed. Furthermore, women could be increasingly blamed for miscarriages and defects in their babies, if their lifestyles would show any deviation from the rules laid down by the medical profession. Eventually, legal prohibitions concerning the behaviour of pregnant women could be extended to many things that a person is normally allowed to do, such as smoking, bodybuilding, love-making and mountaineering. Since these implications are not necessarily acceptable to those who wish to respect feminine autonomy, it seems that Kuhse and Singer have not succeeded in sketching a truly liberal policy for abortion and infanticide.

Feminine autonomy and fairness

Although the theory of Kuhse and Singer may, in its original form, imply slightly illiberal norms, it is not too far removed from a solution which is really capable of making the distinction between abortion and infanticide. It *is* sovereignty over one's body that is important, but not – as these authors allege – the sovereignty of just any human being. The assumption of general privacy and autonomy always attracts the critiques directed against the third premise of the Catholic view presented at the outset of this paper. According to this premise it is wrong to deliberately kill a being which possesses the right to life; according to the criticism put forward by Philippa Foot and Judith Jarvis Thomson this is not necessarily true when the right in question is in conflict with the rights to life and privacy of other beings. But it is only in exceptional circumstances – when, for instance, a woman would die unless an abortion is performed – that this critique justifies termination, whereas it would no doubt be considered generally wrong to kill one being worthy of respect because another one's privacy might otherwise be violated.

What is needed here is a reminder of the fact that *feminine autonomy* in reproductive matters extends the limits of general privacy and sovereignty, since restrictions in this area would create an *unfair disadvantage* for fertile women as opposed to men, children and infertile women.[24] It would be one thing to state that parental autonomy does not justify a freely chosen life-style when it may be harmful or lethal to one's unborn offspring, if the burden implicit in the statement were equally divided among humankind. But it is quite another thing to claim that one group of people, namely fertile women, can be systematically subjected to severe violations of their bodily sovereignty, when, at the same time, the rest of their fellow human beings will never have to face even the threat of similar violations. The unfairness of the situation gives feminine autonomy the extra weight that is needed in drawing the line between the morality of abortion and the immorality of infanticide where healthy human offspring are concerned.

The fact and moral norm that women are not allowed to kill their healthy children after birth does not violate women's rights, since the same facts and norms also apply to other people. Thus, by forbidding infanticide society does not create unfair disadvantages upon groups which do not differ, in the moral sense, from other groups. However, the prohibition of abortion, even if abortion means the killing of a viable fetus in the womb, *would* create such a disadvantage, and should therefore be rejected. Women's right to abortion, in this analysis, would cease to be a right to direct individual self-defence in the case of unwanted pregnancies, which is the label many liberals like to attach to it, and turn it, instead, into a right to *indirect collective self-defence* of the female population against sexist societal norms.

Conclusion

In sum, the content of my argument has been the following. Liberal abortion policies are, quite rightly, based on the premise that fetuses are not persons, and do not possess a right to life equal to that of the majority of adult human beings - if they did, abortions could not be allowed save in some special circumstances. Furthermore, although most fetuses are potential persons, this does not change the situation: the status of potentiality as a basis for ethical considerations can be defended in many ways, but none of these is convincing. The problem with this line of argument is, however, that defenders of moderate and restrictive abortion policies can draw attention to the non-personhood of the newborn infant as well as fetuses, and claim that the termination of pregnancies on request will also lead to the granting of permission to kill babies at will.

Three alternatives have been presented for distinguishing morally between abortions and infanticide, but reference to the attitudes of people towards babies or to general individual autonomy does not suffice to support the division. But a difference can be found between the cases by introducing the concept of feminine autonomy, or feminine liberty from sexist oppression. Women's collective right not to be unfairly burdened because of their reproductive abilities guarantees the morality of abortion while retaining, at the same time, the immorality of infanticide. If there is a dark side to liberal abortion policies, then, it must be sought elsewhere.

Acknowledgements

Parts of this paper were presented at the First International Conference on Philosophical Ethics in Reproductive Medicine, Leeds, England, April 18-22, 1988. My thanks are due to Mark Shackleton and John Calton, Lecturers in English, University of Helsinki, for kindly revising the language of the paper. I am also grateful to Professor Georg Henrik von Wright (University of Helsinki), Dr. Helga Kuhse (Monash University) and Professor Peter Singer (Monash University) for their helpful comments regarding early versions of the paper.

Notes

1. Hayry M. and Hayry H. (1987), pp. 31 ff.
2. Foot (1981); Thomson J.J. (1971).
3. Tooley (1972), p. 44.
4. Singer (1979), pp. 82-83.
5. Noonan (1970), p. 51; Ramsey (1970).
6. Callahan D. (1970), pp. 414, 417, 441n8.
7. Holbrook (1985); Grene (1968).
8. Singer (1979), p.120.
9. Harris (1985), p. 11.
10. Harris *op. cit.*, p. 12.
11. Gordon (1976).
12. See Hare (1975); Bayles (1976); Sher (1977).
13. Brandt (1974), p. 166.
14. Tooley, *op cit.*, pp. 55f.
15. The loud objection that will be raised at this point is that it is, in fact, not a matter of moral indifference if an undesirable result is brought about by acting or by refraining. Our moral duties, so one more precise formulation of the objection goes, fall into two absolute categories. We have positive duties, or duties to positive assistance, and negative duties, or duties to non-interference, and it is always more seriously wrong to neglect a duty of the latter kind than it is to neglect a duty of the former kind. It may well be, for instance, that we are under no obligation to actively produce new human life, but it is nevertheless our duty

not to kill human beings which already exist, such as fetuses.

The difficulty with this objection is that it is based on blurred intuitions and misleading examples. There are, of course, some clearly 'positive' duties as well as some clearly 'negative' ones. For instance, Frank has a strict negative duty not to kill his wife. If he buys a gun and shoots her dead, what he does is most seriously wrong. On the other hand, George has only a minor positive duty to keep his wife alive. George lives in England and his wife lives in Australia, and even if he knows that she will probably die of a kidney disease unless he travels over to donate one of his own kidneys, he does nothing morally outrageous by staying in England. What he does by not travelling to Australia may be wrong, of course, but not nearly as seriously wrong as what Frank does by killing his wife.

This pair of examples gives us rather convincing evidence in favour of dividing duties into positive and negative. But there are many differences between the cases of Frank and George which do not exist between abortion and abstinence from procreation (cf. Tooley 1972, pp. 59-60; Thomson J.J. 1973). First, a doctor performing abortion does not ordinarily have the kind of evil motivation which Frank is supposed to have in murdering his wife. Secondly, there are so many things George would have to do in order to save his wife that it is perhaps unfair to demand that he should do them all. On the other hand, say, a healthy married couple only have to forget about contraceptives in order to procreate maximally. And thirdly, while George can hide himself behind other people's backs ('Why me? Aren't there any kidneys in Australia?'), the healthy married couple cannot, since it is, within the present argument, everybody's duty to procreate, regardless of what other people do. And it may well be that the moral difference between the cases of Frank and George derives from these additional differences concerning motivation, effort and the possibility of passing the duty to someone else.

If we eliminate the additional differences, the cases of Frank and George can be reduced to such forms as Judith Jarvis Thomson's example of the moral symmetry of acting and refraining:

1. Frank hates his wife and wants her dead. He puts cleaning fluid in her coffee, thereby killing her.

2. George hates his wife and wants her dead. He puts cleaning fluid in her coffee (being muddled, thinking it is cream). George happens to have the antidote to cleaning fluid, but he does not give it to her; he does not save her life, and she dies. (Thomson 1973, pp. 158f).

In this pair of examples, there are no significant differences in motivation, in effort, or in the number of people who would be responsible for carrying out the duty. Nor is there a moral difference any more. What George does by refraining is morally as bad as what Frank does by acting.

The question of acts and omissions, killing and letting die, intentionally and unintentionally killing, are further discussed in e.g. Glover (1977) and Kuhse (1987).

16. The contents of this section have been borrowed from Hayry M. and Hayry H. (1989).
17. Singer and Dawson (1988), pp. 98f.
18. Kuhse and Singer (1985), pp. 189-97.
19. Cf. however Kuhse and Singer (1989).
20. Warren (1988), p. 39.
21. Warren *op.cit.*, pp. 32, 39.
22. Kuhse and Singer (1985), pp. 190f.
23. Kuhse and Singer *op.cit.*, p. 191.
24. Cf. Law (1984), cited in Dworkin (1989).

8 Maternal-fetal conflicts: Narrowing the controversy

Frances H. Miller

The more that medical science can offer patients, the more doctors usually want to do. Unique problems arise, however, when the patient is a fetus. In that case the doctor has two charges, and their interests may not coincide. The recent medical, legal and philosophical literature contains abundant speculation about potential conflict between a pregnant woman's right to decline unwanted medical treatment, or to pursue a lifestyle that may compromise fetal well-being, and her fetus's interest in starting life in the healthiest state possible.[1] The controversy is not merely theoretical: within the past two years highly publicized litigation seeking to compel pregnant women to subordinate their 'right' to refuse medical surveillance or treatment, regardless of the impact of that refusal on their fetuses, has ensued in both the United States[2] and Great Britain.[3]

The developing fetuses in both those cases were presumably healthy. The opportunities for conflict between maternal and fetal interests are expanding, however, to include potentially impaired offspring because medical science now permits the fetus to be examined and treated as a patient in its own right.[4] Some fear that recent litigation just scratches the surface of potential controversy, because fetal diagnostic techniques[5] and treatment procedures are improving rapidly and dramatically.[6] This paper takes the position that, when properly analyzed, any substantial conflict between maternal and fetal interests which courts or legislatures might be called upon to resolve may be more apparent than real.

This paper will develop a framework for narrowing the instances in which Anglo-American courts or legislatures might entertain the idea of imposing medical treatment designed to enhance fetal health over the objections of a pregnant woman. The paper deliberately sidesteps the moral quagmire surrounding the abortion issue.[7] It assumes that most courts and legislatures would permit abortion prior to viability when the woman's health would be seriously compromised by continuing the pregnancy. Thus society already recognizes that her rights take precedence over fetal survival under at least this minimal set of circumstances. The paper also assumes that a developing fetus is a proper subject for judicial concern at any stage of gestation, and that fetal interests carry more weight as the pregnancy enters its final stages. It does not, however, assume that the fetus is a person with the full panoply of rights commonly associated with personhood.

Since the pregnant woman and her developing fetus are inextricably intertwined in a physical sense - at least at the current stage of human gestational technology and ethics - any medical treatment designed to aid the fetus must unavoidably involve the woman as well. Thus the stage for conflict is set. Some forms of therapy are designed to help the fetus indirectly by improving maternal health through such techniques as prescribing specific vitamins for metabolic disease, giving blood transfusions, or administering drugs to prevent premature labour.[8] In other situations, drugs are prescribed for the woman only because they are intended to circulate through her bloodstream to reach the fetus. More dramatic forms of intervention can now be performed *in utero* on the fetus itself, but procedures such as surgical insertion of shunts to permit drainage in cases of fetal hydrocephalus[9] require at least some invasion of the mother's body.[10]

This paper does not address the specific issue of maternal lifestyle choices which may injure fetal health.[11] There is no longer scientific doubt that a pregnant woman's behaviour - such as smoking or drug abuse or obesity - can harm fetal well-being.[12] But enforced behavioural modifications, even when relatively minor, require continuing surveillance and control over pregnant women. Such long-term deprivation of personal autonomy raises an additional set of liberty and privacy issues that are beyond the immediate scope of this paper.[13] Indeed, the English Court of Appeal has recently indicated its unwillingness to act in such circumstances without specific Parliamentary authorization.[14]

Notwithstanding the foregoing discussion, most pregnant women are anxious to improve the health of their developing fetuses. Even discounting altruistic concerns for the well-being of future offspring, presumably few non-addicted women would knowingly choose to shoulder the burdens of caring for an impaired child when those burdens are easy to avoid by following medical advice. Most pregnant women will thus ordinarily be willing to undergo medical procedures or treatment designed to improve fetal health, so long as the risks to them and their fetuses are slight. This assumes full explanation and understanding of the actual or potential medical problem, and of the benefits and risks of the proposed course of therapy. In cases reported in the United States, pregnant women seem to refuse consent to treatment strongly advocated by their doctors primarily when the risks are significant and/or the results uncertain,[15] or when their religious beliefs conflict with proposed therapy.[16]

The analytical structure which follows attempts to limit the number of situations in which courts or legislatures might countenance requiring treatment 'for' the fetus over the objections of a pregnant woman. Respectable authority exists on the one hand for the proposition that the woman's wishes should automatically prevail whatever the relative risks and benefits to her and her fetus, because her right as a human being to personal autonomy should be virtually absolute.[17] On the other hand, some scholars argue that once a pregnant woman has decided to carry her fetus to term, she has waived full rights of autonomy and in certain situations may be required to subordinate her own wishes to fetal interests.[18]

This paper takes no position on the ultimate question of whether a court ever ought to order fetal treatment over a pregnant woman's objection; it is designed instead to illuminate the most important issues in the analytical process of determining which instances might warrant intervention, and the order in which those issues might most fruitfully be considered. When analyzed appropriately, most apparent conflicts should resolve themselves without the need for judicial proceedings.

The proposed framework for analyzing the conflict presented when a pregnant woman declines to undergo medically recommended treatment or procedures intended to benefit her fetus proceeds in six stages. It starts, however, from the presumption that a pregnant woman has the same right possessed by any other person under Anglo-American jurisprudential systems to refuse unwanted medical treatment for good reason, bad reason, or no reason at all.

A long line of cases, usually cited as beginning with *Schloendorff v. Society of N.Y. Hosp.*,[19] has affirmed the common law right of patients to be free from unwanted medical intrusions unless the rights of innocent third parties might be seriously compromised.[20] In the United States this right to medical autonomy has important constitutional ramifications as well.[21] The burden of overcoming the presumption that a pregnant woman can refuse medical treatment thus lies with those who would challenge it on behalf of the fetus.

The first four stages of the analysis focus on fetal rather than maternal interests, and narrow the potential candidates for intervention to those where there could be a reasonable basis for believing that fetal concerns *might* have sufficient importance to compete with the pregnant woman's preferences. The last two stages concentrate on the intensity of the woman's interest in controlling her own autonomy. They are resorted to only after the first four stages reveal whether the fetus has *any* claim strong enough to compete with the woman's presumed prerogative of personal sovereignty.

Stage 1: Is the proposed treatment experimental? (i.e. not yet proven to have therapeutic potential for the fetus). If yes, the woman's wishes take precedence and the inquiry ends. If no, go on to stage 2.

Stage 1 rests on the premise that if scientific inquiry has not yet established more than a theoretical possibility that fetal health might be improved if a pregnant woman is compelled to undergo unwanted treatment, under *no* weighting of their respective interests should fetal concerns prevail. Even where the proposed therapy constitutes a *de minimis* encroachment on the woman's autonomy, such as requiring a single vitamin shot, the law should refrain from intervening.

Coerced medical intervention of any sort violates fundamental Anglo-American notions of personal freedom, and physicians who force treatment on unwilling patients without justification[22] may be found guilty of committing battery. Forced medical treatment should thus be resorted to - if at all - only for the most compelling of reasons. A theoretical possibility that fetal health might be improved by a proposed intervention does not meet that standard. Moreover, medicine is an inexact science; even when procedures and therapies acquire scientific legitimacy they sometimes thereafter lose it when additional medical evidence accumulates.[23] It would be unconscionable to force a pregnant woman to subordinate her right to control her own body - a right which is virtually absolute for every competent person[24] who is not pregnant - to the mere unproven chance that her fetus's health might thereby benefit.

Stage 2: Is the threatened harm to the fetus of doing nothing relatively insignificant, or easily reversible after birth? If yes, the pregnant woman's wishes predominate, and the inquiry ends. If no, go on to the next stage.

When the ultimate consequences to the fetus of inaction are relatively minor or transitory, there seems little justification for overriding a pregnant woman's refusal to consent to treatment. In this circumstance fetal interests carry minimal weight in comparison with the frontal asault on self-determination that would inevitably accompany compelled submission to medical procedures or other treatment.

Stage 3: Does the proposed treatment pose significant danger to the fetus? If yes, the pregnant woman's preferences prevail and the inquiry ends. If no, go on to the next stage.

If the proposed intervention exposes the fetus to significant danger of either injury or pregnancy termination, the fetal stake in requiring the pregnant woman to undergo the procedure is weakened substantially. In fact, if a guardian *ad litem* were appointed to protect fetal interests the guardian might well argue against the procedure notwithstanding its potential for conferring benefits. If the fetus itself has strong conflicting interests, those that coincide with the pregnant woman's preference only strengthen the case for permitting her wishes to predominate.

Stage 4: Is there a significant chance that the treatment will be unsuccessful? If yes, the pregnant woman's wishes prevail, and the inquiry ends. If no, go on to the next stage.

If the possibility for the intervention's success is not high, the reasons for requiring it over the pregnant woman's objections are correspondingly diminished. Even though the benefit of a successful intervention might be substantial, the probability of improving fetal outcome bears directly on the issue of whether a woman ought to be forced to subordinate her own autonomy to advance her fetus's health. Statistical probability guidelines are too rigid to be determinative in their own right, but as a starting point one might posit that if less than a 50-50 chance that an intervention will be successful exists, the pregnant woman's wishes should prevail.

After these first four stages of the analysis designed to evaluate the strength of fetal interests have been completed, focus of the inquiry shifts for any conflict not resolved during this narrowing process. At this point it will be assumed that the fetal interest carries sufficient weight to merit some consideration in comparison with a maternal preference for non-intervention. The inquiry now shifts to evaluating the strength of the competing maternal interest.

Stage 5: Does the proposed treatment pose significant dangers to the pregnant woman? If yes, her wishes should prevail and the inquiry ends. If no, proceed to the final stage.

When dangerous medical procedures are advocated primarily for the benefit of third parties, Anglo-American courts have not compelled individuals to undergo them against their will.[25]

> For a society, which respects the rights of one individual, to sink its teeth into the jugular vein or neck of one of its members and suck from its sustenance for another member, is revolting to our hard-wrought concepts of jurisprudence.[26]

Whatever might be the case if recommended therapy poses minimal risks to a pregnant woman, once those risks become substantial it would be unconscionable to compel her to subordinate her own health to that of her fetus.[27] If society will not compel a parent to risk his own health for his *born* child, principles of basic equity dictate that it should not force dangerous procedures on a prospective parent for the benefit of an *unborn* child.[28]

Stage 6: Is the proposed treatment highly invasive to the pregnant woman? If yes, the woman's preferences prevail and the inquiry ends. If no, a court or legislature might countenance requiring her to undergo the therapy.

The greater the degree of invasiveness of medically recommended procedures, the more intense the assault on an unwilling patient's personal autonomy. Not only must a pregnant woman's will be overborn to carry out unwanted treatment, but her physical integrity must be violated as well. Forcing a woman to take undesired medication is concededly offensive to notions of personal autonomy, and systemic medication certainly travels throughout the entire body. But such compulsion pales in comparison with the spectre of a pregnant woman being physically subdued for an unwanted surgical procedure not even designed to benefit her own health.[29] The violence inevitably associated with invasive procedures militates persuasively against their imposition on unwilling patients.

Only if all of the foregoing questions have been answered in the negative does this analysis suggest that it might be appropriate to consider imposing treatment designed to benefit a fetus on a pregnant woman who refuses her consent. The proposed analytical structure should narrow those potential candidates for intervention to a bare minimum. The wild card in the analytical process, however, is the fact that a pregnant woman possesses the power to abort her fetus - legally or illegally - or to flee the jurisdiction should she find such compulsion intolerable.

Since abortion or flight is almost always possible, the more effective - and humane - approach is that of persuasion. The physician has the best opportunity to affect fetal outcome by increasing the patient's understanding of the medical problem and offering sympathetic counselling. The better a pregnant woman understands potential dangers to fetal and maternal health, and the risks and benefits of recommended treatment, the more likely she is to accept medical advice. Compulsion, even as a last resort, is an ethically unattractive alternative.

Acknowledgement

A somewhat different version of this paper appeared in *Seminars in Anaesthesia*, Vol. X, No. 3, 1991, pp. 157-162. The Editors are grateful to the Publishers of that journal for permission to publish the revised version in the present volume.

Notes

1. See e.g. Lowe (1980); Nelson, Buggy & Weil, (1986); Nelson and Milliken (1988); Robertson (1983); Note (1987).
2. *In re A.C.*, 533 A. 2d 611 (D.C.D.C. 1987) (terminally ill cancer patient, twenty-six weeks pregnant, compelled to undergo caesarean section in a [futile] attempt to save the fetus), *vacated* 539 A. 2d 203 (D.C. App. 1987), *remanded* 573 A. 2d 1235 (D.C. App. 1990) ('in virtually all cases the question of what is to be done is to be decided by the patient - the pregnant woman - on behalf of herself and the fetus').

3. *Re F (in utero)*, [1988] 2 All ER 193. (court has no jurisdiction to grant wardship status for unborn child of mentally ill woman, alleged to be incapable of acting in best interests of fetus).
4. See e.g. Murray (1987).
5. See Milunsky (1989), ch. 20-23; Mennuti (1989).
6. Goldberg (1989).
7. *Cf. Webster v. Attorney General of Missouri*, 109 S. Ct. 3040 (1989).
8. See Elias and Annas (1987), ch. 10, for a general description of currently available fetal therapy.
9. Depp, Sabbagha, Brown, Tamura and Reedy (1983).
10. See Lenow (1983).
11. See e.g. Zuckerman *et al* (1989); Chasnoff *et al* (1989).
12. *Re D (a minor)*, [1986] 3 WLR 1030 (local authority, in petition to take baby into care from custody of drug addicted mother [and father], can have regard to addicted baby's 'neglected' condition prior to birth).
While apparently no United States law expressly criminalizes fetal abuse, or conduct by a pregnant woman which recklessly endangers the physical well-being of her fetus, many commentators insist that such legislation is warranted. See e.g. Parness (1988). But see Note (1988).
13. For a well documented discussion of these liberty and privacy concerns, see Note (1986).
14. *Re F (in utero)*, [1988] 2 All ER 193.
15. *In re A.C., supra n. 2.* One commentator states that U.S. courts have ordered at least eleven caesarean sections over the objections of pregnant women, but only *In re A.C. and Jefferson v. Griffin Spalding County Hospital Authority,* 274 S.E.2d 457 (Ga. 1981) resulted in published opinions. Gallagher (1987).
16. *Raleigh Fitkin-Paul Morgan Memorial Hospital v. Anderson,* 201 A. 2d 537 (N.J. 1964) *cert. denied* 377 U.S. 985 (1964). (blood transfusion ordered for pregnant Jehovah's Witness).
17. See Rhoden (1986b).
18. See Robertson (1985).
19. 105 N.E. 92 (N.Y. 1914).
20. See, e.g., *Jacobsen v. Massachusetts*, 197 U.S. 11 (1905) (upholding compulsory vaccinations over religious objections); and *Hughes v. U.S.*,

429 A. 2d 1339 (finding minor surgical intrusion to remove bullet from criminal suspect reasonable).

21. See e.g. *In re Conroy*, 486 A.2d 1222-1223, 1229 (N.J. 1985). Cf.*Cruzan v. Dir. Missouri Dept. of Health*; 1990 W.L. 84074, June 25, 1990.
22. For example, the patient's incompetency could constitute justification under appropriate circumstances.
23. Failure to follow medical advice may turn out to be the more prudent course of action even when procedures or therapy have progressed from experimental to allegedly therapeutic status. Consider the following example taken from a situation arising in the 1960s: 'Janet M., a diabetic, refused her DES treatment, prescribed as especially important in the prevention of miscarriage among diabetics .. she refused to limit her weight gain ... to under thirteen pounds ... and twice refused to show up for scheduled x-rays, citing a distrust of medication and radiation.' (Rothman 1986, p.25), (DES is a drug commonly prescribed to prevent miscarriage in the 1960s, now thought to cause vaginal cancer and other abnormalities in the offspring of mothers who took it.)
24. *Cf. Cruzan*, n. 22, *supra*.
25. *Bonner V. Moran*, 126 F. 2d 121 (D.C. Cir. 1941) (parental consent required for child's skin graft needed to benefit badly burned cousin).
26. *McFall v. Shimp*, 10 Pa. D. & C. 3d 90 (Allegheny County Court. 1978) (court refuses to compel unwilling family member to donate bone marrow to cousin dying of aplastic anaemia).
27. Cf *Rochin v. California*, 342 U.S. 165, 172 (1952) (conviction for illegal possession of morphine reversed where evidence was obtained when doctor forced an emetic through a tube and into the prisoner's stomach against his will) ('Illegally breaking into the privacy of the prisoner, the struggle to open his mouth and remove what was there, the forcible extraction of his stomach's contents - this course of action by agents of government ... is bound to offend even hardened sensibilities. They are methods too close to the rack and the screw to permit of constitutional differentiation.')
28. Surgery to correct congenital fetal hydronephrosis would constitute such a dangerous

procedure. It requires abdominal surgery on the pregnant woman in order to remove the lower fetal body. The fetal ureters are dilated and ureterocutaneous anastomosis is performed. The fetus is then returned to the uterus, but must be delivered thereafter by caesarean section, with its attendant anaesthesia, infection and hemorrhage risks. Harrison, *et al.*, (1982)

29. *Taft v. Taft*, 446 N.E. 2d 395 (Mass. 1983) (four-months pregnant woman with incompetent cervix cannot be forced to undergo repair by cervical cerclage).

9 Organ transplants and anencephalic infants

David Lamb

Introduction

Anencephaly (which means literally no brain) is generally defined as the congenital absence of skull, scalp and forebrain (cerebral hemispheres). In most cases its cause is unknown, but it occurs early in embryogenesis during the first two weeks gestation. Most anencephalic infants are still-born, only between 25 and 45 per cent are live births. About 40 per cent of those born alive survive for twenty four hours. In rare cases they have survived for weeks or months. Only the live births are relvant for organ donation. Anencephalic infants are not dead according to brainstem or whole brain criteria for death. With brainstem function they can breathe, blink, swallow, react to painful stimuli, and possibly suckle. Nevertheless, they do fall into a category of handicapped infants for whom nothing can be done and many believe that great efforts should not be made to prolong their lives. In many hospitals, allowing their natural death is routine.

In this paper four policy options for dealing with anencephalic organ donors will be critically examined.

1. Maintain cardio-respiratory support until death of the brainstem

Current moral and legal guidelines regarding anencephalic infants indicate that removal of organs is illegal whilst they are alive. Their usual mode of death is cardio-respiratory failure which renders them unsuitable for organ donation. To maximize successful organ harvesting under existing guidelines involves the employment of either brainstem or whole brain death criteria, which would necessitate putting the infant on a ventilator. Moreover, the maintenance of ventilation for a period following a diagnosis of death would also be necessary because permitting the infant to cease breathing naturally would result in the impairment of appropriate organs. This intervention creates further problems of its own. In some cases ventilation is likely to prolong the infant's life and may even allow its brainstem to become strong enough to sustain independent breathing for weeks, even months. However, there are indications that the lives of these infants are not unduly prolonged by ventilation, although much more research is clearly needed on how anencephalic infants die.

One argument against this policy is that the interest in the anencephalic infant is strictly determined by an overriding interest in the welfare of the organ recipient, which amounts to the charge that the anencephalic infant is not treated as an end in itself. In reply it can be argued that the therapy employed is not aimed at shortening the life of the potential donor, whose inevitable dying process is simply delayed in order to maintain the viability of salvageable organs. Of course, the therapy is useless from the standpoint of the anencephalic infant, but this seems innocuous so long as there is no breach of the imperative to provide comfort and care for hopelessly incurable conditions. On these terms the management of anencephalic donors is not dissimilar to the management of other catastrophically brain injured individuals maintained in intensive care units in the expectation of brain death for the sole purpose of organ removal. In such cases, for both the potential adult donor and the potential anencephalic donor, the policy is to provide optimal care for the dying patient whilst life can be sustained and then, when further therapy is useless, there is a shift in emphasis from the prolongation of life to the maintenance of organ viability.

2. Re-define brain death in terms of higher brain formulations

The policy of waiting until brain death has been properly diagnosed and confirmed inevitably involves a loss of transplantable organs. Under these circumstances why wait until the brainstem ceases to function? Why not harvest the organs earlier? But existing guidelines prohibit such a course. However, a redefinition of the boundary of brain death in accord with higher brain formulations would mean that anencephalic infants, lacking most higher brain structures, although possessing relatively intact brainstems, could be diagnosed as dead. Accordingly organs could be harvested without accusations of euthanasia or dissection of the living.

This proposal attempts to avoid entanglement with euthanasia by acknowledging death before loss of brainstem functions. Its fundamental premise is that being beyond conscious life, unable to think or have experience of pain, anencephalic infants do not have any identity as persons. Neurologically speaking they are alive but do not have a life. Under these circumstances, anencephalic infants should be classified under modified brain death guidelines, so as to facilitate organ removal. Thus in 1988 there were proposals to amend the American Uniform Declaration of Death Act, which insists on a diagnosis of 'whole brain death ... including the brainstem', to classify anencephalic infants as dead. It should be stressed that these proposals were not designed to prevent doctors from prolonging hopeless and unendurable lives, since many anencephalic infants are routinely allowed to die. These proposals were simply to facilitate organ removal.

One objection to this proposal is that higher brain formulations of death are indeterminate and lack diagnostic certainty (Lamb, 1990). It is also claimed that the proposed redefinition is motivated by a need for transplantable organs rather than respect for the needs of the dying infant. This would simply confirm the opinions of those who have consistently opposed brain death definitions on the grounds that they are a charter for transplant surgeons. To introduce seemingly *ad hoc* redefinitions of brain death, so as to include infants with viable organs, is to invite doubt regarding well-established claims regarding the clinical and theoretical objectivity of brain death.

It might be contended that the motive behind such a redefinition is morally commendable, and fulfils an imperative to maximize the greatest good at the expense only of those who are incapable of obtaining benefit. From this standpoint the interests of those who will surely die without transplants overrides those for whom no improvement can be made. Accordingly a redefinition of brain death would simply facilitate the maximization of the greatest benefit.

The objections are overwhelming. It makes the boundary between life and death dependent upon whatever utility is required. It introduces a situation where the interests of the wider community actually determine the criteria by means of which a person is deemed to be alive or dead. Such a course would go in the face of all currently held beliefs on the separability of decisions concerning the fate of the potential donor from the needs of the transplant team and would be a regressive step away from the principle of individual care.

A more general objection might be made on utilitarian grounds. There are good reasons for the prediction that a definition which allows warm, pulsating, and respirating beings to be regarded as dead would be counter-productive to the procurement of organs. At least when brainstem death has been determined relatives can be informed and shown how the heaving chest and other apparent vital signs are only functions of the machines, and cease as soon as the bodies are disconnected. Relatives can be truthfully told that switching off the equipment does not cause death which has already occurred. But any relaxing of the criteria would produce levels of uncertainty, such that relatives would never know whether the infant was really dead at the time of organ harvesting.

The foregoing objections to the proposed redefinition of anencephaly in terms of a 'higher brain' formulation of death are neither negative nor conservative. They express an ethical commitment to the value of individual care and entail policy consequences that efforts should be made to improve provisions for care of the dying anencephalic infant whilst, at the same time, taking steps to ensure that such infants can become organ donors *after* a satisfactory diagnosis of brainstem death.

3. Define anencephaly as a special legal and moral category

The third policy option is to define anencephaly as a special moral and legal category, such as 'brain absent' (Harrison, 1986). Hence anencephalic infants could be regarded as a potential organ source without violation of brain death guidelines, and, presumably, without accusations of euthanasia.

An initial objection is that it involves a step away from the principle that donors of vital non-regenerating organs should be dead prior to dissection, introducing a category of living beings who have no interests in keeping their organs. Whilst the arguments in favour of harvesting organs from live anencephalic infants are based on maximizing the number of possible lives that could be saved, the argument against is deeper and expresses concern over the very meaning of life and death. When facing a situation where one has to choose between saving a life at the expense of losing something abstract like that status which society attributes to the concept of life, most people would naturally choose to save a particular life. Real lives are more important than abstract lives. But the issue is not that simple. To save lives it may be necessary to regard some lives as disposable. For example, the lives of assailants who are killed as a means to self-defence, or in those horrendous circumstances where starving sailors have been known to draw lots to determine lives which had to be disposed of in the interests of others. But these are extreme circumstances which in no way justify the adoption of an ethical principle which endorses the view that some lives are inherently disposable in the interests of others. One of the reasons is that one can simply go on adding categories of disposable lives as the needs of others increase. Why, in this case, stop with anencephalics? One can easily envisage a situation where special categories can be formulated to include victims of other neurological disorders, who may all become involuntary organ donors. Moreover, once special categories are introduced, where beings are deemed to have no interest in their organs, why only consider organ transplantation? No doubt someone, somewhere, is working out the potential benefit to mankind of using anencephalic infants for experimental research; they are obviously more suitable than laboratory animals.

The case in favour of designating anencephalic infants as members of a special category has been advanced by The Ethics and Social Impact Committee of the Transplant Policy Center, Ann Arbour, Michigan (1988), who argue that, provided free consent from the parents was given, then anencephalic infants, whose future is radically limited, should become organ sources immediately, and not ventilated until brain death criteria were satisfied. The clinical basis for this recommendation was that: 'infants born with the top half of their brains missing are so very different from other living infants', and because:

> anencephaly is a condition so special, so very different from all others, and one whose diagnosis and prognosis can be established with such manifest certainty, that infants in this most unfortunate condition should be viewed as in a class that is entirely *sui generis*, and for which special rules and laws should apply. (Ethics and Social Impact Committee, 1988, p.28).

Among the merits of this proposal is that it respects the existing definition of death and openly confronts the issue of 'dissection of the living' rather than the endorsement of 'definitional gerrymandering' in order to avoid charges of euthanasia and homicide.

The ethical basis of the proposal is the view that anencephalic infants do not have interests which overrule those possessed by other human beings. Allegedly lacking consciousness, rationality and will, they cannot be regarded as 'ends-in-themselves', and hence are not protected by the second form of Kant's categorical imperative, which prohibits using others as means to an end. Hence:

> in the case of brain-absent infants, there is no *possibility* of awareness, the physical equipment being totally missing. Thus, in this narrow class of cases, there can be no question

about possible human consciousness because it is a physiological impossibility, even during the first few hours before brainstem activity also ceases. (Ethics and Social Impact Committee, 1988, p.29).

There are, on these grounds, 'no intrinsic interests of anencephalics to be defended'. (ibid. p.29). It would seem that these infants have even fewer interests than laboratory animals, since they are deemed to be incapable of having any experiences.

Despite the initial attractiveness of the proposal to consider the 'brain absent' anencephalic infant as a special moral category, there still remain very serious doubts. How unique is anencephaly? Is it easy to diagnose? Can we be absolutely certain that anencephalic infants cannot experience pain and discomfort? Is there absolute proof that even the most rudimentary levels of consciousness are absent? And has the Committee satisfactorily rebutted the *sorites*, or slippery slope, objections with their claim that anencephaly is a determinate category?

The claim that anencephaly merits a special moral category rests on assumptions concerning the clinical homogeneity of this condition. But although it is easily recognized in most cases, like various non-cognitive states it manifests itself on a continuum; at one extreme there may be no cerebral tissue at all, and at the other there is rudimentary cerebral function. The brainstem in anencephaly displays a spectrum of involvement, from normal to absent. According to most sources diagnosis is fairly obvious, and it can be detected quite easily in pregnancy. But not all cases are so straightforward. Unlike the diagnosis of brainstem death, there is no operational definition that includes all cases of anencephaly and excludes everything else. One of the leading textbooks on the subject says that: 'an almost incomprehensible array of synonyms and classifications exists in the literature; many exclude entities now considered to be pathogenetically unrelated to the anencephaly spectrum'. (Lemire, Beckwith, and Warkang, 1978, p.5). In his account of the differential diagnosis of anencephaly Shewmon outlines overlaps between mero-anencephaly, micro-anencephaly and encephalocele, which could be problematic for the classification of anencephaly as a unique condition, as the latter 'constitutes a continuous spectrum of its own, at the other end of which are encountered quite functional individuals'. (Shewmon, 1988, p.12).

If these clinical differences are not maintained, if concern is primarily with non-improvement, or as the Ethics and Social Impact Committee put it, a 'future which is so radically limited', then there is a risk of a slippery slope from anencephaly to other neurologically impaired conditions, and eventually all dying patients. Already some physicians have expressed an interest in harvesting organs from hydranencephalics, who usually survive much longer than anencephalics, as they 'are actually likely to be *more* attractive sources of organs because of the extra time for development'. (Quoted by Capron, 1987, p.7).

It should be stressed that in the vast majority of cases anencephaly is easily diagnosed. But the force of *sorites* objections to the citing of anencephaly as a unique case is bound up with those borderline cases where overlaps may produce diagnostic and conceptual uncertainty. It has been pointed out that:

> There is no anomaly that cannot be misdiagnosed, and this holds particularly true for anencephalic infants. For example, one baby entered into Loma Linda University Medical Center's protocol was later referred back to an out of state medical center when LLUMC doctors determined the baby was not a true anencephalic. (Willke and Andrushko, 1988, p.32).

It should be pointed out that criticism of the consequences for the anencephalic infant, and fears of the expansion of the category of potential donors to infants with less severe defects, (following 13 failed attempts to obtain organs etc. from such babies) led to a suspension of the LLUMC programme. (Shewmon, 1989).

Turning to the questions whether anencephalic infants are capable of experiencing pain and discomfort and whether it can be established that they do not possess even rudimentary levels of consciousness, it is instructive to compare these states with normal infants. Since they share similar neural structures that mediate typical newborn behaviour, anencephalic infants with relatively intact brainstems exhibit many behavioural patterns similar to normal infants, such as; 'purposeless back-and-forth movements of the extremities, sucking and swallowing, normal orofacial expressions to gustatory stimuli, crying, withdrawal from noxious stimuli, and wake/sleep cycles'. (Shewmon, 1988, p.13). Whether consciousness and a capacity to suffer exist is a philosophical question which is not answerable by reference to empirical evidence. There is, however, evidence that despite absence of higher brain structures, the brain stem is capable of much more complex integrative activity than is usually attributed to it, including some functions generally considered to be 'cortical'. (Shewmon, 1988, p.14). This suggests that one cannot safely assume complete absence of more primitive forms of awareness in anencephalic infants. That is to say, one cannot, with certainty, rule out the possibility of sub-cortical structures taking over certain 'cortical' functions. And as more is learnt about the brainstem function, of its greater complexity than was hitherto thought, there is a need to maintain an open-minded approach to the possibility that the subjective experience of anencephalic infants, like their external behaviour, may resemble more those of normal newborns than of older PVS [Persistent Vegetative State] patients. (Shewmon, 1988, p.14). At the very least anencephalic infants are similar to the laboratory animals - with smaller brains - whom we are obliged to treat humanely.

4. Is there a need for a moratorium on anencephalic organ transplants?

The case in favour of a moratorium is based on the commendable motive that one should not take steps into an ethically uncertain area until the issues have been resolved.

But where does this uncertainty lie? During the past twenty years the case for clear-cut guidelines regarding the determination of brain death has been well established by physicians, philosophers, lawyers, and the lay public. (Pallis, 1983, Kennedy, 1988). During the past decade a similar debate has taken place with regard to the clinical reliability of tests for the brainstem concept of death and the need for an objective definition has been clearly established as a separate issue from the need for transplant organs. (Lamb, 1978, 1985, 1990). Against this background the plea for a moratorium on anencephalic transplants simply pushes the clock back to a period of uncertainty and confusion between criteria for death and the needs of the transplant team.

Recent guidelines for neonatal transplantation in the UK indicate that 'absence of spontaneous respiration would signify death', a view which is shared by Canadian authorities (Salaman, 1989, p.623). When formulating guidelines for the determination of death in neonates, and hence criteria for cadaveric organ removal, it is important to maintain a strict analogy with brain death in adults. Despite difficulties in diagnosing infant deaths, as a matter of logic there can only be one form of death. With adults brain death is determined with reference to irreversible apnoea and irreversible loss of consciousness. The same, no less, should apply to infants. In the case of anencephalic infants the absence of forebrain together with irreversible apnoea should meet the requirement for a strict analogy with adult brain death. In this respect it would seem that the guidelines of the UK Working Party of 1988 are satisfactory insofar as they recommend that 'organs for transplantation can be removed from anencephalic infants when two doctors who are not members of the transplant team agree that spontaneous respiration has ceased' (BMA Working Party 1988). At this point the dead infant may be ventilated for the purpose of organ procurement and the analogy with adult brain dead organ donors maintained.

The poor quality of an anencephalic infant's life might be cited as evidence against any imperative to keep it alive against all odds. For example, non-treatment of spinal lesions in anencephalic babies is considered acceptable (King, 1987, p.101). And at least one Roman Catholic moral theologian has recognized that it may be a moral misunderstanding to try to sustain the life of such an infant (McCormick, 1974). The President's Commission have indicated that therapy for anencephalic or cephalodymus infants is 'futile', (President's Commission, 1983, p.219-220). In a similar vein the BMA's Working Party to Review Guidelines on Euthanasia noted that:

> Any move towards liberalising the active termination of a severely malformed infant's life would herald a serious and incalculable change in the present ethos of medicine. Nevertheless, there are circumstances where the doctor may judge correctly that continuing to treat an infant is cruel and that the doctor should ease the baby's dying rather than prolong it by the intensive use of medical technology. (BMA Working Party, 1988, p.1377).

But these guidelines for selective withholding of therapy are based on considerations of the interests of the infant in question, not on the potential benefits its organs may provide for others, however commendable such a course may appear. Quite clearly, the problems concerning therapeutic options for anencephalic infants test the very limits of the principle of individual care, and force discussion on what to do in 'hopeless' cases. But given the possibility that, in the long term, pre-natal screening may shift the moral decision-making to an early stage in fetal development, a fundamental revision of values which forbid the procurement of organs from living patients (on which public acceptance of organ transplantation rests) should be resisted. Equations based on the benefits of the many against the inability of a dying infant are easily weighted against the latter. But if accepted they could shift ethical priorities to the point where the benefits of others encroach on the duties to individuals. On these terms the ultimate consequences of proposals to dissect live infants for the benefits of others could undermine the rationale of transplant surgery, - its 'do no harm to the donor' principle - exacerbate public fears of transplant surgeons as 'organ vultures', and contribute to the gradual exploitation of the vulnerable.

10 Public attitudes and the treatment of neomorts

Christopher Tindall

In a widely-publicised case in North America the heart of an anencephalic newborn was transplanted into another infant which needed the heart to live. The donor, Baby Gabriel, had been diagnosed as anencephalic in the womb. One day after birth she was attached to a respirator, and declared brain dead three days later. But the body was kept functioning on the respirator for a further 41 hours whilst being flown from Canada to the United States, where the surgery was performed at Loma Linda University Medical Center.[1]

This case sparked one controversy regarding the use of anencephalics as organ donors. But it also contributed to another on-going controversy, this due to the publicity it received, regarding the maintenance of the brain dead in a stage of simulated life before organs are removed.[2] It is the second of these controversies that I intend to address in this paper. The concerns expressed seem to be twofold: (i) that organs are taken from 'living' bodies; (ii) that the future consequences of accepting this procedure may be undesirable. I will make some remarks pertinent to the first of these concerns, but the focus of my paper will be the second. I will look particularly at the claim, made most clearly by Douglas Walton, that a respect for the human body ought to prevent us using the brain dead for anything more than the harvesting of organs, and that the thought of any further use is repugnant to us. I will suggest that there is no good reason against proceeding further, that any intuitions of repugnance that we may have against doing this have no real moral foundation, and that the benefits to be gained from doing so are reason to proceed.

I

Initially, there is some question of whether those declared brain dead are actually dead with no possibility of consciousness. Cases of people who have claimed to have heard their own deaths pronounced only to be revived and our inability to clearly define what death is underlie the seriousness of this concern. The thought that people who have been declared brain dead might still 'feel' things is a real cause for alarm. But if we stipulate at the outset how we are to understand brain death, much of this concern can be alleviated. Confusion resides in the question whether the person is still alive when the body is artificially animated. What a person is and in what personhood consists are questions that arise whenever the origin or termination of life is at issue. They are relevant to the brain-death debate but are unlikely to be resolved by it. What is clear is that at a certain stage of brain deterioration the possibility for personhood is irreversibly lost. In spite of strong arguments supporting a criterion of human death in terms of loss of higher brain formulations,[3] there is still an insistence in the literature (and, we are led to believe, in practice) favouring some criteria of whole-brain death. David Lamb, for example, points to the difficulty of proving total absence of sentience when the brain stem is still functioning.[4] Lamb himself defines death as the 'irreversible loss of function of the organism as a whole',[5] thereby encompassing both the cognitive functions associated with higher parts of the brain and the integrative functions associated with the lower parts of the brain. Douglas Walton also adopts a view of whole-brain death.[6] For the most part, I shall stay clear of this debate, focussing more on the consequences of using neomorts than the criteria for determining them. I stress whole-brain criteria here only because it tends to allay fears that a person might still be alive when organs are removed - fears rooted in the possibility of someone being aware of what is happening to them and feeling pain - and it is these fears that are most relevant to my discussion.

There is, though, a further consideration, most clearly expressed by Hans Jonas. It is important because it might well affect the way society perceives brain death. Jonas refers us to the traditional criterion of death as the irreversible cessation of cardiorespiratory activity and points out that the brain dead body is quite simply still alive by this criterion. As he says, the body is 'arrested on the threshold of life and death'.[7] This is obviously true since it is quite necessary for the kinds of procedures being considered (organ removal, etc.). But how much this should count is questionable since, as I have noted, the death of the person is not synonymous with the death of the body, just some critical aspect of the body.[8] The human organism, which is what the brain-dead cadaver is, is no more a person than it is a human being.[9] Simulated life is still life, as Jonas insists, but it is not the expressed life of a person. Although we might agree, given our ignorance of what constitutes death, that 'a definition cannot substitute for knowledge',[10] what we do know is that with cases involving the irreversible loss of the whole brain there is no possibility of awareness or of pain.

What is significant in Jonas's remarks, however, is his portrayal of the brain dead cadaver as 'animated', breathing, 'alive', because this emphasizes how it will *appear* to people generally. They will picture accurately a vital functioning human organism, and this will affect the way they respond to this issue. I will return to this consideration later in the paper, where it will play an important role.

II

I turn now to the principal focus of my paper: will the harvesting of organs from brain-dead cadavers lead to repugnant practices involving abuses of those cadavers?[11] The belief that this will but should not happen is correctly identified by Douglas Walton as a slippery slope argument against maintaining brain-dead cadavers in a state of animation.[12] The question is whether this is a good or legitimate slippery slope argument.

In a 1974 article[13] Willard Gaylin anticipates some consequences that might follow from the combination of new technology[14] with the definitions of brain death. While the person is dead, the body continues to function. With whole-brain death, the external support of respirators is required to keep the heart beating and the lungs breathing; with cerebral death, the comatose body can function on its own.[15] Gaylin imagines such brain-dead bodies being maintained and put to use in 'bioemporia'. Here, the totally 'person-like' bodies serve as excellent subjects for the training of young medical students; for the testing of new drugs; experimenting on the immune system; for banking blood cells and organs; for the harvesting of the same; for the manufacturing of hormones and antibodies; and for much more. The benefits of the bioemporia are enormous and they avoid any need to experiment upon conscious human subjects and animals. Yet, in spite of all these possible benefits, Gaylin draws attention to the repugnance of the entire enterprise, the feeling that it may dimish our humanness.

The repugnance is anticipated by Jonas who uses it, along with the argument already discussed, to support his insistence that brain-dead bodies not be used as organ donors. While Gaylin constructs a possible scenario, Jonas goes further in presenting a full-fledged slippery slope argument. If the brain-dead body is no more than a corpse, then all possible benefit might be extracted from it. Accepting this premise, he argues, there is no logical reason to turn off the respirator after needed organs have been removed. The body may be kept on call as a bank for further organs, a blood-bank, an instrument for surgical and grafting experiments, and the other uses also mentioned by Gaylin.

People may not be thinking this way, notes Jonas, but he has shown that it is conceivable. And later he asserts that the licence which a definition of death as brain death allows will make these consequences irresistible. Hence, he believes they will occur if not prevented. 'It follows', he writes, 'that interventions as I described should be regarded as on a par with vivisection and on no account to be performed on a human body in that equivocal or threshold condition'.[16] To avoid the slippery slope the first step should not be taken: respirators, if in use, should be turned off when death is declared.

Douglas Walton does not believe that Jonas's Slope is warranted, that the consequences listed by Jonas (and Gaylin) must follow. The critical need for suitable organs is a compelling and sufficient reason not to turn off machines until *after* useful organs have been removed. Walton does not believe the subsequent abuses envisaged by Jonas will follow because he is convinced that it will be possible to maintain and police a policy of respect for the brain-dead body. The ground for this conviction seems closely related to the repugnance evoked by Gaylin's bioemporium. It has nothing to do with the possibility that the person is still alive, as Jonas fears. Walton firmly rejects this in cases where the criteria for whole brain death have been correctly applied. Rather, Walton appeals to a basic respect for the human body. We *ought* to respect it and never treat it indecently or carelessly. Consequently, he insists, to maintain brain-dead cadavers beyond the stage of organ removal is unethical.

This respect for the human body has a certain intuitive appeal to it, and it has often been cited as a reason for some policy or action, or, perhaps more frequently, *against* some policy or action. In 1978 the U.S. Department of Transportation found that the use of cadavers in the testing of airbags 'violates fundamental notions of morality and human dignity'.[17] In spite of the importance of the information gained by using cadavers, and without any clear argument other than the appeal to intuition, the programme was discontinued.

More interesting, because it records a wider response and is a direct predecessor of Gaylin's scenario, is the history of cadaver use in medical training and research. Much has been made of the public reaction to anatomical research and the practice of dissection in nineteenth century Britain. The so-called 'Dead Body Bill' which aimed to procure cadavers for the various schools of anatomy in London was the occasion for an enormous out-pouring of public outrage. As M. J. Durey explains in recording the history of that bill, there was already popular feeling opposed to anatomical research, but the attention it received during the debate over Henry Warburton's Anatomy Bill brought it to a new peak of intensity.[18] But much of the initial opposition seems quite reasonable, fueled as it was by the insensitive pranks of medical students and the widespread fear of 'burking'.[19] Neither stimulus of the outrage had anything to do with the actual practice of anatomical research.

It is true, as Durey notes, that Warburton had to contend with a more informed wave of humanitarian sentiment. But this was principally spawned by sympathy for the poor since, on Warburton's proposal, it was the bodies of those who died in poor-houses that were to be made available to the anatomists. There was further deep concern over the manner in which the remains were discarded. But again, in both these responses, the sentiment of opposition was not against anatomical research or dissection *per se*.

I go into this case in such moderate detail here in order to press home the lack of any *clear relevant argument* to support popular repugnance. The arguments that emerged tended to be of this practical thrust. The closest one comes to an argument supporting real sentiment is in the position of the Tory philanthropist M.T. Sadler who argued, as Durey conveys it, 'that dislike of dissection was not a prejudice but a natural feeling which could only be destroyed at the expense of some of the best feelings of human nature'.[20] Prefiguring as this does the remarks of Jonas, this comment is important, but it is also vague and remains to be explored.

There are of course strong religious grounds giving support to the senses of repugnance and respect being discussed here. While such support might have only a limited impact in a secular society, it would go part way to explaining the presence of the sentiment. Robert Veatch has recently pointed to the obvious significance of the corpse for a religion like Judeo-Christianity, with its emphasis upon the resurrection of the body. But Veatch also notes that few Christians interpret this doctrine literally and most are able to circumvent it in some way.[21] Likewise, Orthodox Judaism accepts autopsy only when it will aid the living, and requires that organs be returned for burial. Such a doctrine excludes its adherents from the kinds of possibilities being discussed in this paper. But in doing so it simply extends prohibitions that are now in place and that oppose what is already accepted by the majority of people of differing or no religious persuasion.

What we require, then, is a clear argument to support the general intuitions about respect for the body. It must be granted that the intuition alone does not constitute a reason, although it does motivate us to search for reasons. Accordingly, Walton is to be commended for actually putting forward two arguments in support of his belief. It is to these that I now turn.

His first argument involves an analogy advanced against what Walton perceives as the weak premise in the slippery slope. Assuming only persons have rights, then: If X does not have rights, we are under no obligations or duties with respect to the treatment of X.[22]

Contrary to this, Walton insists that we are under obligations and have duties to the treatment of nonpersons that are not seen to have rights. To support this he gives as examples obligations to preserve forests and natural park land and the duties we have toward animals, 'obligations not to be cruel to them and so forth'.[23] He does not elaborate on these examples, he simply presents them with no more detail than I have given here. But he insists that they falsify the suspect premise given above.

Now, what must be remembered is that X in the present case is a brain-dead cadaver and what while Walton may be able to give some support to a general claim that we have obligations and duties toward some nonpersons, he needs to show *specifically* that we have such obligations and duties toward brain-dead cadavers. The latter do not seem to be like the environment and animals. The obligations we have toward the environment are unclear. Walton has not elaborated them and I believe the onus is on him to do so if he wishes to convince his audience. With respect to animals, however, he is more forthcoming. We have a duty not to be cruel to them. But surely we hold that it is wrong to treat animals cruelly because they can feel pain and are capable of enormous suffering. Thus, although they are not persons, there are restrictions on what we should do to them. Here, however, is a critical dissimilarity between animals and brain-dead cadavers. As Walton has amply argued, brain-dead cadavers cannot feel pain and are not capable of suffering. If the reason we should not be cruel to animals is because they can experience pain, then this undermines the effectiveness of Walton's analogy.

Such an argument does have force in some contexts. It answers, for example, Mary Anne Warren's contention that because fetuses and newborns are not persons and hence not members of the moral community, there are no moral restrictions on what can be done to them.[24] Since newborns and fetuses beyond a certain stage of development can feel pain and suffer, and are like animals in this respect, then we might well have duties and obligations towards *these* nonpersons. But the best conclusion that Walton's analogy is able to support is that *some* nonpersons ought to be respected. It does not follow from the evidence provided that we have duties and obligations toward *all* nonpersons, and we have good reason not to consider brain-dead cadavers among those to be included.

Walton provides a second argument which can be called the 'proximity' argument. Having reiterated the claim that the practice of maintaining brain-dead cadavers in a state of biological activity without urgent necessity is unethical, he gives the following reason:

> I believe that such a practice could be unethical because a neomort, even if not a person, once was a person and still bears a proximity of relationship to the person it was. Although it may not have the rights of a person, we are obliged to treat it with dignity out of respect for the person it once was.[25]

What is crucial here is the nature of this proximity. Unfortunately, Walton is not able to tell us much about it. It is, he concedes, 'not easy to specify'. The most plausible suggestion is the corporeal association between the cadaver and the person it once was. The cadaver more than resembles the person (as a statue might), it actually was or contained the person. However, Walton is unable to tell us more about the relationship of identity or containment, other than to note that it requires more attention if it is to be 'adequate to our intuitions'.[26] Lamb makes some attempt to provide further attention when he points out that we generally consider it worse to mutilate a corpse than a statue of the deceased.[27] But although this may be true, it does not tell us why we hold this belief. So the 'proximity' argument remains unfinished. In the end it is offered only as a reason which might account for our intuitions about the treatment of brain-dead cadavers. We fear the abuse of brain-dead cadavers because we see in the cadaver vestiges of the person it was or contained. But whether this is something to be noted about the cadaver itself or merely a psychological fact about ourselves remains to be considered.

Before proceeding on this line of inquiry, let me make two further observations about Walton's second argument. First, even if we accept some form of proximity argument as reason for respecting brain-dead cadavers and not proceeding down Jonas' slippery slope, it is not, once again, a reason for respecting *all* brain-dead cadavers. Rather, it pertains only to those have have been persons or in which personhood has been contained. If we return to the case with which I began this paper, we might note that while baby Gabriel, the anencephalic newborn, is certainly a human being, it is difficult to accept her as a person. In what would her personhood consist? She has developed no character, no self-awareness, no values or beliefs, no plans, etc., and these are some of the characteristics by which we recognise persons. So Walton's second argument would not be a reason for respecting the brain-dead cadavers of newborns. Second, we need to look closely at what Walton is doing. He is trying to justify an intuition, the same intuition which accounts for the repugnance elicited by Gaylin's bioemporium. Now something strange suggests itself here. Walton accepts the use of brain-dead cadavers as organ donors, but rejects further non-urgent uses because he finds these intuitively distasteful. But what Gaylin is suggesting, and Jonas is insisting, is that the *whole enterprise,* including the transplantation of organs, is distasteful.[28] The repugnance seems to cover any and all uses of brain-dead cadavers. The intuition arises early for Gaylin and Jonas; in Walton it is postponed by his recognition of the urgent need for donor organs.

III

In effect, Walton's repeated reference to the intuition that it is wrong to abuse the dead suggests that, despite his claims to the contrary, he is not really as concerned about the mistreatment of the dead as he is about the effects the idea of such mistreatment has on the living.

From the recent literature on harming the dead an argument advanced by Joan Callahan stands out as almost simplistic in its persuasiveness.[29] She reasons that we cannot harm decedents because they are not subjects and that we carry out the wishes of the dead usually not out of respect for them but because those wishes coincide with other values we hold important.[30] Although she is not considering harming or wronging the dead in quite the same physical sense which concerns Walton, insofar as he invokes the memory of the person a brain-dead body once held or was, and insofar as he appeals to our intuitions about harming the dead, her further argument is quite relevant to the issue. She insists that any intuitions we have about harming the dead cannot be genuine moral convictions. If there is no subject, there is no one who can be harmed, and so there is no good philosophical reason for believing the dead can be harmed. Consequently, these stubborn intuitions are 'judgments we are inclined to make simply because we *think of* the dead as the persons they were *ante mortem*. They are sentiments which are to be accounted for psychologically'.[31]

This claim, that our intuitions about the dead are rooted in sentiment and not moral conviction, acquires greater importance when we further consider that having respect for brain-dead cadavers would not necessarily preclude using them in all the ways Gaylin and Jonas envisage. Walton assumes that these imagined uses are necessarily abuses, but there is nothing *prima facie* to suggest that we could not employ brain-dead cadavers with enormous respect and gratitude, that we could not, as Walton himself says, 'maintain and police a policy of respect for the human body apart from the question of whether the body is alive'.[32]

What this brings us to are the sentiments of society, where the intuitions which concern us are shared. And we might ask, in spite of Callahan's insistence to the contrary, whether indeed these sentiments cannot in some way form genuine moral convictions, or at least play a significant role in public policy concerning the use of brain-dead cadavers for organ transplants and other beneficial purposes. Should, in other words, the repugnance felt at the thought of Gaylin's bioemporia count for anything?

Joel Feinberg considers the import of sentiment in his paper 'The mistreatment of dead bodies'.[33] Gaylin's suggestions evoked widespread repugnance in some of Feinberg's students and this moves him to consider whether there are grounds for prohibiting such schemes based on appeals to the harm principle and liberty-limiting principle. The most important of his considerations involves his response to one of William May's arguments opposing the routine salvaging of organs from the dead.[34] May's key argument--adapted by Feinberg to include a liberty-limiting principle as a premise--is that such salvaging offends a sentiment which is essential to our humanity.[35] Whatever weakens the tendency of people to experience repugnance in some circumstances is a bad thing because the weakening of that tendency degrades human character. There are, May believes, natural human sentiments toward dead human bodies and the salvaging of organs from the brain dead, if made routine, would erode these sentiments.

In response, Feinberg notes that May's argument proceeds in a vacuum, taking no account of the benefits to be gained and the harms to be prevented by harvesting the dead. If there is no countervailing consideration, then a practice which weakens natural human sentiment should be avoided. But in this instance the prevention of deaths and suffering is a sufficient countervailing reason to allow the practice. Furthermore, Feinberg doubts that the routine salvaging of organs would erode essential human sentiments because it would be done openly and respectfully by professionals who would take the same approach to their work as pathologists or embalmers.

This general view is shared by Jonathan Glover in the report of the committee he chaired for the European Community.[36] He suggests it is unlikely that the surgeons who remove organs from people care less about ordinary people. With respect to the weighing of values, Glover places people's needs for replacement organs over any intuitive feelings of respect for bodies and concludes (writing here of fetal transplants) that 'it seems perverse to place respect for bodies before rescue for the living'.[37] When introducing his Anatomy Bill, Warburton expressed a similar utilitarian viewpoint in arguing that even a hostile public opinion should in some circumstances be overridden by needs of the state.[38] Warburton's bill was passed in August, 1832.

It is worth remembering, however, that Walton had been prepared to permit the harvesting of organs from brain-dead cadavers for just the kinds of utilitarian reasons that Feinberg and Glover offer. Walton's concerns relate to further uses of the bodies which, although mentioned in his discussion of Gaylin, Feinberg does not consider in his own arguments.

One current advocate of the importance of public sentiment is Mary Warnock. In Britain, the Committee of Inquiry into Human Fertilization and Embryology, which she chaired, repeatedly took note of public sentiment in formulating its proposals. This was, Warnock explains in her Introduction to the Committee's *Report*,[39] because neither utilitarianism nor a blind obedience to rules could respond to the questions the Inquiry faced.

This may be so, but it is also the case that Warnock feels deeply that morality cannot be separated from feelings. She invokes Hume, who insists that moral distinctions are drawn not by reason, but by moral sense.[40] And she appeals to Lord Devlin's belief that the law must prohibit conduct which the public finds repellent and to his defence of the shared moral view as the cement that binds society together.[41]

Elsewhere, in addressing the issue of surrogate motherhood, she proposes that those who do not wish to live in a society in which women become pregnant for money have a right to have their feelings respected. In fact, she goes so far as to argue that feelings can amount to a moral view (contrary to the opinion expressed by Callahan) and that morality does not have to be a matter of reason. To this end she writes:

> Indeed the whole notion of reason, on the one hand, and feeling or sentiment on the other, essentially opposed to each other, seems to me to be a mistake--a hangover from an eighteenth-century way of looking at things. I don't see

> why a moral view cannot be both grounded in feelings and at the same time (in some suitably broad sense) be rational, or at least not irrational.[42]

However, it is one thing to say that feelings must be respected as rational, and something else to argue that there is a public morality rooted in sentiment which ought to be respected by law. It is important to clarify Warnock's position. At least, it is important for what I want to suggest.

Warnock does believe that if there are actions which offend against prevalent moral opinion, then these have the potential of harming society. Such morality-dependent harms are important and weight should be given to them in deciding policies. But giving weight to such considerations does not mean that they should be made the exclusive determinants for deciding what should be done; it is wrong to see the tyranny of the majority lurking behind Warnock's arguments. As Michael Lockwood points out in discussing Warnock's views, allowing a principle of respect for society's moral beliefs to operate without restrictions could have undesirable consequences. Warnock wants to include with this principle considerations of utility and individual liberty.[43] In fact, Lockwood believes that a principle of respect for individual liberty is already contained within Warnock's principle of respect for moral beliefs. The principle that people have the right to shape their world in accordance with their conception of the good can be seen on the individual level as personal autonomy and on the collective level as democracy. Both are variants of self-determination. On these terms it is inconsistent to claim that individual liberty can ever be legitimately constrained in the name of the prevailing morality. This, suggests Lockwood, would be self-determination at war with itself.[44]

Still, we can agree that feelings ought to be respected without allowing that they constitute a moral view. A moral view requires depth and even Lockwood accepts that intuitions must meet minimal standards of rationality before they can be taken seriously. In the end, he cannot give an unqualified answer to the question of whether Warnock's view is right or wrong.

In fact, I believe that we need to distinguish Warnock's desire to respect people's feelings from any belief in a 'common morality', and that this is a distinction we need generally to see as important. After all, while finding merit in the impetus behind Devlin's earlier proposals, Warnock cannot overlook the enormous problem inherent in his views--that the idea of a 'common morality' may well be a myth. Accordingly, she concedes that there is no agreed set of principles that everyone, or the majority of people, hold to be true, and this is the case especially in new areas like embryology (and, we might add, the use of brain-dead cadavers).[45] Consequently, when she talks about public sentiment she is not talking so much about an expressed moral view as a 'corporate reaction'. For example, on the subject of research on human embryos she writes:

> Society, insofar as it is a single identifiable body, has here, perhaps uniquely, a corporate reaction. It is one of fear. People generally believe that science may be up to no good, and must not be allowed to proceed without scrutiny, both of its objectives and its methods.[46]

This, I suspect, is the negative sentiment which people share when faced with the details of things like the use of brain-dead cadavers for organ transplantation. It is not so much a sense of moral wrongness as it is a vague fear of the scientifically unknown and the sense that their environment is changing in ways that they do not understand and they may not like. If this is what Warnock means when she says that the feelings of people ought to be respected when planning public policies, and I believe it is, then there is every reason to agree with her. It also gives us a handle on how to proceed if we feel it is important to combat these sentiments on behalf of the benefits which they threaten.

IV

Public sentiment counts because people may indeed be harmed if practices that conflict with that sentiment are allowed to continue. But if there is no expressed and common morality grounding that sentiment (and there is no reason to believe there is) and there are benefits to be derived from the practice in question, then steps should be taken to both prevent the morality-dependent harm which might occur as a result of harvesting the brain dead for organs and to ensure that the benefits such a practice makes possible are not jeopardized.

Contrary to what Walton implies, there is nothing *intrinsically* wrong with the acts under consideration. And I mean not just the use of brain-dead cadavers for organ transplants (since, after all, Walton does not find this wrong), but also the further uses imagined by Gaylin and abhorred by Jonas. Any wrongness associated with such acts has nothing to do with the person the body once held or with brain-dead bodies being like animals. It has to do only with the harm it might cause the living.

This harm can be avoided if efforts are taken to educate the public in the fact that, as Feinberg notes, the sentiment does not work in a vacuum. There are the benefits of life for some and the prevention of suffering for others. And these benefits follow not just from using brain-dead bodies in situations where organs are in urgent need. The less urgent needs of research and physician-training are also important to society.

Gaylin and May are concerned about our humanity. May believes the routine salvaging of organs will erode natural human sentiments. Gaylin balances the specific benefits of the bioemporium against spiritual and abstract costs, implying that we risk the abandonment of 'dignity for dollars'. But this is not the only possible effect which the use of brain-dead cadavers might have on our humanity, and there is a more positive perspective from which to view this issue. Human sentiments are valuable as they help us to recognise and contribute to human goods. Basic to the unfolding and nurturing of our human nature is the care with which we treat other persons and the interest we take in their welfare. And this should extend not just to our contemporaries but to future generations. The uses of the bioemporium suggest benefits over and beyond the treatment of immediate needs; they will be instrumental in providing a healthier, more knowledgeable and less disease-prone environment for our children and their children. Contributing to this human good, and even, I would suggest, recognizing it as a society, strengthens human character. This strengthening is itself a non-tangible benefit which, when added to those tangible benefits already recognized, provides a compelling case in favour of the bioemporium. It is fitting here, I think, to recall Hume's remark that benevolence above all else bestows merit on a human creature and that a part of such merit 'arises from its tendency to promote the interests of our species, and bestow happiness on human society'.[47]

Of course, it would be important to introduce any programme on a voluntary basis. Amendments to various Anatomical Gift acts should facilitate this. It might even initially be advisable, in the sole interests of public promotion of the programme, to allow the concerns of relatives to override the requests of donors, although this would be controversial in its own right, and there is no strong argument for it beyond the pragmatic point raised here.

If the repugnance felt at the suggestion of the bioemporium and all it entails, the intuition of Jonas and Walton, is actually a veiled but very real fear of the unknown and of science unrestrained, then we need to combat that fear with knowledge. Give people an understanding of the procedures involved in keeping the brain dead ventilated. Show them that procedures will be performed openly and with respect, on bodies that neither are nor contain persons. This will not be easy because, as Jonas emphasized, the brain dead are warm, animated, person-like bodies, and this is a captivating image. It will be difficult to override the association of personhood with this image and any change in public attitude should not be expected to occur overnight. But it is in our interests to remove this fear and encourage a gradual evolution of public perception. And we are quite justified in doing so, as I hope to have shown in this paper. When this change of perception has been effected, then the benefits of Gaylin's bioemporium can be appreciated without guilt.

Notes

1. This occurred in the Fall of 1987. For a journalistic report on the case and the associated controversy see 'A life-giving death', *Maclean's Magazine*, November 2, 1987, p.45. For a discussion of the case as it bears

on the treatment of anencephalic infants, see Walters and Ashwal (1988).

2. There is, of course, some difficulty in establishing the anencephalic as brain dead, if by this we mean whole-brain death including the brain stem. By definition, the anencephalic does have a functioning brain stem, although both cerebral hemispheres are missing. But an early death is inevitable without respirator support (and not long in occurring even with it). In fact, Fritz Beller and Julia Reeve have argued in their (1989), that the whole-brain definition of death is not appropriate for the anencephalic since no real personal brain life can be achieved. The anencephalic has never possessed any of the brain tissue necessary for a minimal cognitive life and, hence, they propose, has not lived and cannot die.
   This however, leaves the anencephalic in a curious ontological state that will not be discussed here. Suffice to say, medical centres like that at Loma Linda University have procedures whereby anencephalics on respirators are disconnected every 3-6 hours to determine the absence of spontaneous breathing, and thereby to establish death according to the whole brain definition (Beller and Reeve, p.18). [For further discussion of the ethics of using anencephalics as organ donors, see also David Lamb's paper in the present volume.]
3. See in particular Roland Puccetti, (1976) and (1988).
4. Lamb (1985), p.43. Lamb also reports the unpopularity of higher brain formulations among physicians (p.46).
5. Lamb, *op cit.*, p.12.
6. Walton (1980). Although I take issue with some of his arguments, Walton's book represents a thorough introduction to the topic. It should be noted, however, that Puccetti (1988) takes Walton to task over the manner of his commitment to whole-brain criteria.
7. Jonas (1974), p.140.
8. Lamb would disagree here (*op cit.*, p.36). But I find his discussion confusing, since he appears to equate 'person' with 'patient', allowing that the brain-dead cadaver can be both. This implies a looser notion of 'person' than is usual,

although I see no objection to calling the neomort a 'patient'.

9. Michael Lockwood argues persuasively for this distinction in his (1985a).
10. Jonas, *op cit.*, p.138.
11. It may ultimately matter whether permission has been given by the donor prior to death or, after the fact, by relatives. However, this is to some degree a separate matter and I will make only brief reference to it at the end of the paper. I am concerned principally with whether the practice of maintaining brain-dead cadavers in a state of animation ought to be allowed and the conditions appropriate to this.
12. Walton, *op.cit.*, p.37.
13. Gaylin, (1974).
14. It must be conceded here that on current knowledge neomorts could not be maintained in simulated life for the periods of time required for some of Gaylin's consequences. As Lamb notes (*op.cit.*, p.35), asystole, or the cessation of the functional contraction of the heart, usually occurs within days or even hours of brain death, and he cites a Danish study which gives an upper limit of 211 hours (with corroborating studies from Britain and the U.S.). However, Michael Green and Daniel Wikler point out that there is nothing in principle to prevent this interval from being expanded, 'perhaps indefinitely'. Green and Wikler, (1980), p.110).
15. Gaylin is here referring to both whole-brain and neocortical criteria for death. Because of the concerns mentioned earlier, I am in this paper restricting my comments to the former.
16. Jonas, *op.cit.*, p.138.
17. These words of Congressman John E. Moss are cited in Wade, (1978), p.1420.
18. Durey (1976).
19. Named after the notorious Burke, who was hanged in Edinburgh in 1828, and his associate Hare. They supplied anatomists with the numerous bodies required either by robbing fresh graves or by simply murdering people. In spite of strict measures taken by the authorities, the practice repeatedly flared up throughout Britain in the early-to-mid-nineteenth century. In fact, part of the rationale behind Warburton's bill was to make such burkers redundant.
20. Cited in Durey, *op.cit.*, p.209.

21. Veatch (1989), p.200.
22. Walton, *op. cit.*, p.40.
23. *Id., ibid.*, p.41.
24. Warren (1973).
25. Walton, *op. cit.,* pp.45-46.
26. *Id., ibid.*, p.47.
27. Lamb, *op. cit.*, p.105.
28. Jonas reinforces this in his 'Postscript of December 1976', where he cites with extreme disapproval the case of a 17-year-old girl who was pronounced brain dead and then kept on a respirator until after her eyes and kidneys had been removed. He laments that 'the door I tried to keep shut has already been opened'. And he notes that although the respirator was turned off 'to keep it going beyond the first two surgeries would have required no further legitimation and no new decision principle'. See Jonas in Thomas (ed.) (1983), p.314.
29. Callahan (1987) 341-352. See also Levenbrook, (1984) and Pitcher (1984).
30. Actually David Lamb argues that neomorts can be harmed, but he does not do himself credit in this argument, nor would his argument make any useful contribution to my discussion. Lamb writes, for example, 'Cromwell was humiliated and disgraced when his body was gibbeted at Tyburn long after putrefaction had set in' (p.86), and he concludes from this and other examples that 'there is no point at which a person cannot be harmed' (p.87). I find this reasoning quite confused and can see no way in which Cromwell's 'person' could be harmed by the manner in which his remains were treated. Clearly, any sense of 'harm' at work here is not relevant to what concerns me in this paper.
    A more reasonable argument for posthumous harm which has similarities with that of Lamb is to be found in Feinberg (1984). But Feinberg's theory also has its problems, as has been adequately shown in Waluchow (1986).
31. Callahan, *op.cit.*, p.351.
32. Walton, *op.cit.,* p.39.
33. Feinberg (1985).
34. May (1972).
35. Gaylin, it might be noted, mentions May's conviction in a way which implies agreement.
36. Glover *et al.* (1989).
37. Glover *et al.*, *op.cit.*, p.112.

38. Durey, *op.cit.*, p.210.
39. Warnock (1985a).
40. Hume (1978), pp.470-476.
41. See Devlin (1959).
42. Warnock (1985b), p.154.
43. Lockwood (1985b), p.172.
44. Lockwood, *op. cit.*, p.173.
45. Warnock (1985a), p.xi.
46. Warnock, *op cit.*, p.xiii.
47. This quotation from Hume's *Philosophical Works*, IV, 179, is the one with which E.C. Mossner closes his (1980), p.608.

11 Neonatal intensive care: Where and how do we draw the line?

A.G.M. Campbell

Lawyers on both sides of the Atlantic have criticised doctors for taking life and death decisions that seem to pay little attention to 'due process' and sometimes are seen, to the outsider at least, to be arbitrary and capricious, of doubtful ethics and questionable law (Robertson & Fost 1976: Kennedy 1981). However, like so many lawyers, or ethicists, philosophers and theologians, when confronted with the most poignant and most difficult individual cases, perhaps they might agree that doctors have to grapple with questions to which there is no obvious 'right' answer and take decisions that most lawyers including judges are only too happy to avoid. I shall discuss a few aspects of decisions to forego life-sustaining treatment, now major concerns in an intensive care unit at any age but particularly at the 'edges of life' (Ramsey 1978).

Some medical decisions do appear to be taken with less than adequate information; after hurried processes of consultation that leave little time to reflect on the options available, and with inadequate attention to consequences. Some questions need rapid responses. Some decisions also seem to infringe strict interpretations of the law and, from time to time, they reach the courts and are exposed to public debate on both sides of the Atlantic. Decisions made in the heat of battle inevitably show flaws on detailed retrospective analysis. The unexpected birth of an abnormal baby is a shattering experience. Family joy is instantly turned to bereavement and grief and it is the rare doctor or nurse who is not deeply affected by such a tragedy, no matter how hardened by long experience. But on their own, aching hearts, compassion for the infant, and gut feelings are insufficient criteria to decide that a baby should live or die. Cool heads and reasoned argument are needed as well. Increasingly exposed to public view, many medical decisions, albeit with hindsight, need to withstand intense medical, ethical, and legal scrutiny. Many argue that just as war is too important to be left to generals, questions of life and death are too important to be left to doctors.

The questions raised are many and complex - should doctors concentrate on being good technicians and leave those arguments to others? Should they use modern intensive treatments to salvage all infants born alive or should they draw lines and use treatment selectively rather than indiscriminately? Where can lines be drawn and who should draw them? Doctors alone? Parents alone? Doctors and parents? Should others be involved and if so who? Is there a place for ethics committees? When should the law (the courts) get involved?

The technological revolution in intensive care

It is 19 years since Ray Duff and I described some of these dilemmas as we experienced them and attempted to resolve them in the Neonatal Unit at Yale. Although we reported nothing new, we felt it was time to break professional silence on a major social taboo, in the hope that 'out of the ensuing dialogue perhaps better choices for patients and families can be made' (Duff & Campbell 1973). Since then we have been criticized many times because of our failure to be more explicit about which infants are involved in 'selective non-treatment decisions'. In 1979, Sherlock wrote,

> Unless those who favour selective non-treatment for defective infants can develop more precise guidelines and rationales, the fundamental weakness of their position will remain; it will commit us to courses of action and to social policies that are at odds with one of the oldest and most basic moral principles in the medical profession - to provide life-saving therapy to all of those who need it.
> (Sherlock 1979).

But life-saving therapy is a relatively modern concept - it is only in the past few decades that we have been able to do much to save life or alter the time or the manner of death. As Silverman has pointed out it is only relatively recently that the salvage of all infants born alive has been seen as a desirable social goal (Silverman 1981). Even Pierre Budin, the earliest pioneer of special care for premature or what he called 'congenitally feeble' infants dismissed the smallest babies in a couple of sentences, 'We shall not discuss infants of less than 1000g. They are seldom saved and only very rarely shall I need to allude to them' (Budin 1907). Infants with birth defects were known as 'monsters'. No attempt was made to resuscitate them and in the privacy of the home or the hospital delivery room, undoubtedly they were 'helped to die'. Doctors have always been selective in their use of treatment, with or without the knowledge and agreement of parents. In past days of relative medical impotence and paternalistic decision-making, much was left to nature; and if infants did not survive it was generally felt to be for the best. Now that so much more *can* be done, treatment dilemmas figure much more prominently and at times they dominate discussions about the care of individual infants. Questions about the technical complexities of care are much easier to answer.

To understand these remarkable changes in attitude it is necessary to be aware of the dramatic developments in treatment that began in the late 1950s and continue today. Central to the evolution of intensive care was a greater understanding of the pathophysiology of life and death - the realization that death was a process and not an event; that cessation of breathing and stoppage of the heart were potentially reversible, and that death of certain parts of the brain could occur while the body continued to live provided that certain conditions were met - the maintenance of respiration, circulation, nutrition and the prevention of infection - all requiring skills and technology not even imagined when ancient codes of ethics were formulated.

The unprecedented expansion in life-saving technology has brought great benefits to childbirth, infancy and childhood that hardly need repeating here. These recent developments have been paralleled by the increasing necessity for better understanding of the rights and wrongs of using this technology. Our ability to use it in the technical sense has outstripped our sensitivity to the nuances of using it responsibly by paying proper regard to the consequences for patient and family. We hear phrases like 'if it is there it *must* be used' when perhaps the question we should ask is 'should it be used?' It is relatively easy for doctors to become experts in prolonging life, but much more difficult for them to know when to stop or even to start treatment in conditions of medical ambiguity. At times it is tempting for doctors to concentrate only on the technical aspects of care - and leave the ethical and legal hassles to others - but I believe that this abdication of responsibility amounts to a victimizing abandonment of patients at times of greatest need. It violates a prime rule of medical ethics - that we must act in the way which best serves the interest of the patient.

In recent years doctors have tried to increase their knowledge and understanding of ethics, philosophy, theology *and* the law, and by so doing improve the ethical basis for their decisions. In hospitals it is now quite common to hold ethics rounds when the morality of medical decisions takes precedence over the technical aspects of care. Ethics advisers of various kinds, drawn mainly from backgrounds in philosophy and theology, have appeared on wards and intensive care units, particularly in the United States where the 'hospital ethicist' has emerged as a new specialist. Provided he or she is prepared to achieve credibility by 'standing the heat' along with the staff they are welcome, but it is disturbing to read that two things that seem to be of great concern (at least to one ethicist) are status in the hospital hierarchy and the method of payment (Purtilo 1984). Undoubtedly, the past 20 years have witnessed a considerable 'coming together' of medicine, ethics and the law in attempts to resolve ethical dilemmas, particularly those posed by continuing or foregoing life-sustaining treatment, - are we prolonging dying unnecessarily or allowing to die prematurely?

Drawing the line: medical considerations

In any intensive care nursery, infants can be placed in three groups:

1. Those for whom available treatment is usually successful.
2. Those for whom treatment is of doubtful benefit.
3. Those for whom treatment is likely to be futile.

Infants in the first group pose few treatment dilemmas. They form the vast majority of the nursery population at any one time and are treated vigorously from birth with every expectation of success. Decisions about treating infants in the second and third groups are problematic. While aggressive intensive care may ensure survival, for a time at least, it may be at a major cost to the infant and family - perhaps a period of prolonged dying or a life of grievous disablement and handicap. Included in these categories are tiny infants born at the very limits of viability; infants with major birth defects and infants severely damaged by complications of pregnancy or birth.

Perhaps this is an appropriate place to emphasize that foregoing life-sustaining treatment does *not* mean withdrawing *care*. Infants must be given all the attention that we associate with good medical and nursing practice - cherishing, warmth, changing, relief of hunger and thirst and treatments aimed at relieving any pain or distress. Questions about feeding are controversial and emotional. I believe that oral feeds should be given as tolerated, but that once a decision is taken to allow an infant to die it is illogical to prolong dying unnecessarily by introducing intravenous infusions or even tube feeding. In each case there must be considerable latitude for individual circumstances and attention paid to the views and feelings of the parents, and the nurses involved at the cot side.

The tiniest infants

In many ways neonatal intensive care has come to epitomize the success of modern medicine. Nowhere has it been more successful than in the salvage of tinier and tinier infants born prematurely. Neonatal mortality rates have fallen to levels hardly thought possible 30 years ago. Original concepts of fetal viability at 28 weeks gestation are now outmoded. Viability for individual infants is now thought to occur somewhere between 24 and 26 weeks of gestation. Whereas Budin dismissed infants under 1000g birthweight as 'seldom saved', any contemporary neonatal unit will proudly report many infants under 1000g and a few not much more than 500g birthweight who not only survive but are reported to be healthy on follow-up (Powell *et al.* 1986). But success is not just measurable in improvements in survival. Just as we have learned how to resuscitate successfully and prolong life, so we have learned about conditions that damage the neonatal brain, how to correct them and, even better, how to anticipate them, prevention always being better than cure. With more and more tiny babies surviving premature birth it can be said with confidence that their prospects for a healthy life have never been better. Babies born in the 1950s who weighed under 1500g and who survived had less than a 50% chance of attending normal school, whereas we now expect fewer than 10% of surviving infants over 1000g to show significant neurological disability.

> The majority of infants treated in regional neonatal intensive care units in recent years are free of major handicaps. There are two major trends in the outcome of preterm infants -
>
> 1. A decrease in the birthweight at high risk for handicap from 1500g birthweight or less to 1000g or even 750g.
> 2. An increase in the infants who are normal and those who have minor neurological abnormalities (Ellison 1984).

At the present time I view 750g as a flexible 'cut-off' at which we might consider drawing a line at *routine* intensive care while we review the circumstances of the individual infant and discuss the options and likely outcomes, with or without treatment, with the parents. In a recent annotation, I stressed that using any 'cut-off' like this only made sense if it was flexible and, *inter alia*, took into account many other factors such as gestational age, condition at birth, associated abnormalities, complications etc. (Campbell 1982). I also emphasized that continuing improvements in neonatal care made it inevitable that weight or any other criteria must continue to change and pointed out:

> ...we are approaching the stage of gestation when extrauterine survival can be maintained only by using some form of extracorporeal artificial placenta. Almost certainly this could become possible technically, but it might be an important point to "draw the line" while we contemplate the ironies and implications of overlapping with the legal limit for abortion.

Many units treat all infants born alive aggressively whatever the weight or gestational age, but I have not seen any results to date to make me feel that *routine* intensive care is wise either for the infant or for the family who have to live with the consequences. Below 750g at appropriate gestational age the risks of major neurological disability increase considerably. For example, one study which used single and multiple variable analysis showed that the only single variables with a 20-fold or greater increased risk of motor dysfunction of infancy were birthweight under 750g, intracranial hemorrhage, and hydrocephalus, where there was a 99-fold increase in the risk of handicap (Ellison *et al.* 1983).

Abnormal infants

Primary brain defects Specific examples of congenital abnormalities where a decision might be made to withhold or withdraw certain treatments include infants with various forms of primary brain defect - where there has been faulty development of the brain such as anencephaly, hydranencephaly, iniencephaly and extreme forms of hydrocephalus. Certain disorders of the chromosomes result in the birth of infants with multiple defects involving many organ systems including the brain. These infants are easily recognizable, the diagnosis can be confirmed quickly and accurately and they have a limited life span even with treatment.

Perinatal brain damage Many of the brain damaging metabolic conditions of infancy are now being anticipated in certain well defined situations, e.g. hypoglycaemia following intrauterine growth retardation or in infants of diabetic mothers; or identified through mass screening at birth, e.g. phenylketonuria or hypothyroidism. Perhaps the most important example of perinatal damage that in some circumstances still lacks reliable anticipation or prevention, but can be identified quite accurately after birth in some infants, is asphyxial damage from deprivation of oxygen. Ischaemic encephalopathy of the brain and its frequent association, intracranial hemorrhage, remain most important causes of severe neurological damage and eventual handicapping disability. With newer imaging techniques it is possible to identify infants with destructive brain injury much more accurately at a time when the wisdom of continuing life support can be discussed with the parents. A smaller group of infants in this category are those damaged severely by congenital infections such as cytomegalovirus infection or toxoplasmosis.

For some of these conditions, few doctors and nurses familiar with them would argue for aggressive treatment in all cases. Much more controversial is any extension of non-treatment policies to other chromosomal disorders such as Down's syndrome, various forms of spina bifida without gross hydrocephalus, and multiple major congenital malformations that do not necessarily involve the brain, but taken together are likely to seriously affect the infant's future quality of life.

Down's syndrome provides a good example of how the 'ethical climate' can change over a relatively short time period. In the past decade Down's syndrome has been the subject of legal as well as ethical controversy. Unlike trisomy 13 or trisomy 18, where the outlook for life or health is uniformly bad, these children have a wide spectrum of abnormalities and intelligence and given good care may survive to a relatively old age. Most children require special schooling and remain dependent but an increasing number are able to start mainstream education and achieve some independence provided that they receive the appropriate stimulation and support. Within a loving family it would be ridiculous to suggest that they have an unacceptably poor quality of life. A decision to withhold or withdraw life-supporting treatment from such infants should remain the responsibility of doctors and parents but the current climate of opinion in this country and most others is that they should be treated as normal infants. Ethical and legal difficulties are likely to arise only when an infant is rejected by parents or they refuse permission for a life-saving procedure such as an operation to correct a congenital blockage of the intestine. Lasting rejection because of Down's syndrome alone is unusual but parents occasionally reject a life-saving operation because they believe that it is in the infant's own interests not to survive. Whatever the cynical view of others, inconvenience, the effect on the rest of the family or the potential drain on the family's finances are rarely uppermost in parents' minds at this time. In the past I have supported parents who have refused permission for operation but in the current climate a decision to withhold life-saving surgery from an infant with Down's syndrome is likely to be contested by someone and it is unlikely that the courts would find in favour of the parents with or without the support of the doctors (Raphael 1988). Some parents resent such interference in family affairs and remain extremely concerned about the future for their child. For example, who will care for handicapped children if they, the parents, become ill or should die first? They may continue to view their child's early death as preferable to his or her sudden incarceration in an institution and these anxieties may continue to influence them in accepting or rejecting medical advice at any age.

Thus for infants at the borders of viability and infants with congenital defects the most important medical criterion is the degree of abnormality, disease or damage to the brain. If there is little or no prospect of a functioning brain sufficient to allow the child to 'have a life', in Rachels' phrase, rather than merely to be alive, it seems to me that withdrawal of intensive treatment may be the appropriate, indeed the prudent and compassionate course of action. We all recognise the qualities that make us holistic human beings where the whole is greater than the sum of its parts, - sentience, the ability to communicate, to give and receive love, physical and mental control of our own bodies, to achieve some independence etc. That is what parents hope for in their children.

But decisions should not be made on technical medical criteria alone. Before any decision on the 'right' treatment a detailed, expert and thoughtful review by the various health professionals with the family is essential to take into account all pertinent biological and social data.

> A good choice for treatment might be an infant with spina bifida who is wanted, who can be cared for in the family without excessive or coerced sacrifice and for whom the family's caring is loving and voluntary. A "bad" choice for treatment might be a similar infant but where the parents have little or no capacity to care for their child; where the family does not want to be forced to do what they believe should not be done and where resources to help the child or the family are limited or absent (Campbell & Duff 1979).

Drawing the line: ethical considerations

The troubling nature of these difficult dilemmas was eloquently expressed in 1971:

> Decisions made on such grounds are difficult if not impossible to differentiate in principle from decisions made by the Spartans and other earlier societies to expose to nature those infants born with manifest anatomical defects. We are being driven towards the ethics of an earlier period by the inexorable logic of the situation and it may only increase our discomfort without changing our views to reflect that historians and moralists both agree that the abolition of infanticide is perhaps the greatest ethical achievement of early Christianity.
> (Morison 1971).

Infanticide has a long history, indeed it was rampant in this country until quite late in the last century. In 1884 the *Lancet*, a British medical journal, included a commentary entitled 'British

Infanticide' which began, 'We are approaching that indifference to child murder which we are accustomed to think confined to unchristian nations'. (Commentary 1884). The prime candidates for infanticide were defective newborn infants and infants born illegitimately from the sexual exploitation of female servants and factory workers by their male employers. Killing or abandoning an illegitimate child was often the only escape from destitution.

The scandal of infanticide led to the establishment of foundling homes where babies could be left anonymously, but the conditions were so bad that most of the babies died anyway. There was some logic to the infanticide of abnormal infants as the parents were unable or unwilling to assume the burdens of caring for a child who could never contribute to the family or community and, as deformed infants were considered 'non-persons' anyway, the law did not intervene. Giving infants rights including the 'right to life' is a relatively recent development. A child had no intrinsic right to life or protection by nature of being born - value and rights were acquired perhaps only after several years, either through demonstrating the development of intelligence or by acceptance into the community (Amundsen 1987). Thus until relatively recently a severely handicapped child did not have much of a chance, certainly not in a world where even healthy children were subjected to violence, neglect and outright infanticide.

Now we have laws to protect children's rights but the application of these laws to seriously impaired newborn infants remains unclear. When doctors lacked the knowledge and the technology to save or prolong life the law was relatively powerless to shield imperilled children from death. As the ability to save and prolong life has increased so have the difficult moral and legal questions raised by decisions to 'let nature take its course'. The law takes more interest in these issues in the United States. Jeff Lyon in his book *Playing God in the Nursery* refers to the recent Baby Doe decisions in the United States.

> The Doe's decision to let their baby die contained nothing especially novel. Parents, good ones and bad, have been consigning their offspring to death for thousands of years. The new idea was the Reagan administration's - that virtually all babies, however grievous their handicaps, must be kept alive at any cost. (Lyon 1985).

In reviewing the options among ethicists Robert Weir has discussed five (Weir 1984):

1. Treat all non-dying neonates.
2. Terminate the lives of selected non-persons.
3. Withhold treatment according to parental discretion.
4. Withhold treatment according to quality of life projections.
5. Withhold treatment judged not in the child's best interests.

In considering selective non-treatment he prefers the final option. He notes several strengths. *First*, that the position focusses the issue of non-treatment where it belongs: on the birth defective neonate.

> The questions it raises reflect the same focal point: are the available medical treatments in this child's best interests? Will treatment be done - or be withheld - for the child's sake? Is the child's medical condition such that, even with treatment, death will be preferable to a tortuous existence? Or, stated in another manner, the position emphasises that decisions about treatment or non-treatment should focus on the neonate's medical condition, that such decisions concern suffering and irremedial handicap rather than projected social worth, that comparative judgements involve contrasts between injurious existence and non-existence (rather than between abnormal infants and normal ones), and that in some neonatal cases it is justifiable to conclude that treatments should be withheld because life, on balance, will be harmful rather than beneficial to the child.

This option i.e. child's best interests, begs the question implied in 4. Namely, what is the future quality of life for the child? I believe these two options, i.e. quality of life and best interests, to be inseparable, but it is important to emphasize what I mean by quality of life in this context. In their opposition to selective non-treatment, various individuals and groups have distorted and misrepresented this to mean 'worth' in utilitarian terms of costs or benefits to others, 'lives worth saving' or 'not worth saving'. They have also interpreted selective non-treatment for seriously abnormal infants as implying a general policy of discrimination against all individuals with disability or handicap, a distressing and surely undeserved accusation against paediatricians who have been to the forefront in promoting the cause of handicapped children. This hyperbolic propaganda has also been distressing to many families and has been influential in causing quality of life judgments in neonatal treatment dilemmas to be seen as unacceptable or at least inadmissible in American hospitals. Rigid rules (like the so-called 'Baby Doe' regulations in the United States) to prohibit such judgments represent a naive oversimplification of a complex problem. They ignore the practical realities of abnormal birth by implying that disability or potential handicap is irrelevant to medical decision making. When parents and doctors consider quality of life for an infant they do not weigh up an infant's future social utility or worth. Parents have high hopes for their children, they know the kind of life that they want for their child in their child's own interest. As Father Richard McCormick tells it, parents want to know answers to such questions as: 'Granted that we can easily save the life, what kind of life are we saving?' (McCormick 1974).

We talk of infants' best interests as being paramount in the judgment of doctors and parents when making decisions for and against intensive care. From a doctor's moral obligation of beneficence, if a treatment will benefit the infant it should be used. If it will not be of benefit it may not be used. An absolute duty to use treatment may be modified if the price is too high when weighed against the duty of non-maleficence, 'doing no harm'. For infants, these decisions are particularly troubling to ethicists because of the need for proxy decision making. While a competent adult can exercise autonomy, someone else must decide for an infant; and to decide that an infant, no matter how tiny or how handicapped, would be 'better off dead' is indeed awesome.

Some might ask: how is it possible to say that death at the very threshold of life is for a child's benefit? Surely where there is life there is hope, so that treatment to prolong life must always be started or continued, the position taken up by pro-life organisations who have been vigorous critics of 'selective non-treatment', or as I prefer, 'selective treatment'. Sanctity of life proponents, especially those who hold the most extreme positions, believe that all withholding or withdrawing of treatment is wrong unless the patient has been declared dead. A moment's reflection will indicate that to take this position is needlessly cruel and virtually untenable when applied to children who are dying or to infants afflicted with the worst injustices of abnormal birth, e.g. anencephaly and other gross abnormalities of brain development. The late Paul Ramsey, who was prominent in opposing selective non-treatment, believed that the appropriate response to such a dying child is kind and respectful care designed to ease the child's passing. Even Dr. C. Everett Koop, until recently Surgeon-General of the United States and a vigorous promoter of the Baby Doe Rules, drew a line short of an absolute adherence to the sanctity of life. At a hearing before Judge Gerhard Gesell, Dr. Koop, as spokesman for the Department of Health and Human Services, acknowledged that he had been involved in the decision to issue the notorious 'Notice to Health Care Providers' (the notice which promulgated the 'Baby Doe' Rules) but nevertheless admitted that in a child having essentially no intestine or in an infant with anencephaly, only limited nursing care should be provided.

At the opposite extreme of the sanctity of life position is that which considers treatment or non-treatment, survival or death, in strictly utilitarian terms, something akin to the farmer who chooses from a litter the strongest and least flawed and who eliminates the rest, the runts. His decision is based on what is best for him and his herd as regards future productivity and economic yield.

In practice *all* decisions are made somewhere in between these two extremes. We draw lines according to an infant-based best interests standard and use the future quality of life of the infant as an important consideration. According to some critics of course, we do this not on a line but on a slippery slope to infanticide. Perhaps we do play on slippery slopes, but if we do it openly abuses should be obvious, and professional and societal standards of moral behaviour should ensure well defined and reasonably secure footholds.

How do we draw the line?

As far as can be judged, in this country (the UK), most people and most doctors still prefer decisions about foregoing life-supporting treatment to be determined by the doctors and parents after careful individual case analysis and informed discussion. The primarily responsible doctor, usually a paediatrician or neonatologist, in co-operation with appropriate specialist colleagues, must take all necessary steps to establish the diagnosis and estimate the prognosis as accurately as possible. He or she should discuss the issues and options with the junior doctors and nurses who provide the most consistent hour to hour attention to the baby and the parents at the cot side. The family doctor may provide important insights to the parents' understanding of the issues and their ability to cope with the implications of the treatment options. They in their turn may seek the views of grandparents, other relatives, clergymen, friends and perhaps many others. Thus a 'moral community' is created with shared commitments to assume responsibility for examining the issues, making the choices, and living with the consequences (Duff & Campbell 1987).

In spite of all too frequent examples of how parents can exploit and abuse their children, in most circumstances parents are still regarded as the most appropriate decision makers. Compared to others they are more likely to make concerned and loving decisions for the welfare of their infant, if given the facts and options accurately, sensitively and objectively and if given time for reflection. If the child survives and is handicapped, they will be the ones who will have to assume responsibility for future care perhaps for a lifetime - long after the doctors and others have withdrawn.

There will be occasions when even loving parents may make choices that conflict with the infant's best interests. Parents may be so emotionally overwhelmed by the bereavement of abnormal birth that their judgement is affected. They may be unable to understand the complexities of the condition or the treatmemt, so that they may view the future either unduly pessimistically or excessively optimistically, their views perhaps distorted by an unbalanced presentation of the medical facts. Very occasionally they will put their interests and those of other family members first, although, as Shelp has pointed out, that in itself may not necessarily be wrong (Shelp 1986). However it is in these situations that doctors may have to intervene and take decisions contrary to parental wishes, with or without the authority of another agency such as a court of law. Court action in such circumstances is distressing for parents and should be used as a last resort and on good grounds. In most circumstances court decisions are sought to clarify the issues when doctors wish to start or continue treatment against the family's wishes; but occasionally it may be necessary to withdraw intensive care against the wishes of the parents when it is clear to everyone that it is futile, pointless and inhumane.

Withholding or withdrawing treatment: is there a difference?

Some doctors draw a curious distinction between *withholding* life-sustaining treatment and *withdrawing* it once started. In a recent study of approaches to these problems in the United Kingdom, Sweden and the United States, considerable variations in the attitudes of doctors became apparent (Rhoden 1986a). In Sweden, doctors seemed more comfortable with withholding treatment but were reluctant to stop it. In the United States there was a more aggressive approach to life-sustaining treatment in general and American paediatricians were more likely to start intensive treatments on almost all viable infants and continue them until death. They too were reluctant to withdraw, no doubt influenced by Baby Doe and its aftermath.

In the United Kingdom, treatment, even such measures as intubation and intermittent positive pressure ventilation (IPPV) might be started at birth or shortly afterwards on almost all infants but could well be withdrawn later if the infant's subsequent progress suggests that the treatment is unlikely to confer any long term benefit. This seems a logical approach as it gives each infant a chance - 'a trial of life' - while the potential benefits and burdens of treatment are being assessed and discussed with the parents. I do not see any moral distinction whatsoever between withholding treatment and withdrawing it. If information is available to indicate that treatment will not benefit the infant it should not be used and can either be withheld or withdrawn. In the same way if treatment will benefit the infant it is equally wrong to withhold it or withdraw it.

Unlike doctors in Sweden, if there *is* any difference between withholding and withdrawing, I would argue that withdrawing treatment is preferable to withholding it. Starting vigorous treatment gives doctors and parents time for reflection and further discussion on the benefits and burdens of continuing treatment. More information, perhaps based on the results of further diagnostic tests, on the infant's initial progress, or on the development of complications will mean that a decision to withdraw is based on better grounds than an earlier and perhaps premature decision to withhold.

Although in some respects it seems particularly daunting and emotionally upsetting to the staff to call a halt to aggressive treatment, it should be less difficult to justify if a proper process of decision making has been carried through, as particular care will have been taken to reduce to a minimum the small but inevitable degree of uncertainty that remains with all these difficult decisions.

The philosophical, medical and legal confusion over withdrawing and withholding may also influence decisions in a potentially dangerous way. If it is emotionally or medico-legally more difficult to withdraw than withhold, doctors may withhold treatment simply because of the difficulties they face in trying to stop treatment later. Thus at birth, when there is considerable uncertainty about the outcome for a very low birthweight infant, IPPV may be denied when it might be extremely beneficial. Thus withholding and withdrawing should be considered as having equal weight medically, morally and legally. If treatment is not believed to be in an infant's best interests or may cause harm it should not be given and may be withdrawn. If it will benefit the infant it must be started and should not be withdrawn.

The reluctance of American paediatricians to stop treatment except in the most extreme situations is understandable given the current medico-legal climate in that country. Sadly, self-interest and the interests of the institution may now take precedence over the interests of the infant and family. It is going to take courageous decisions by individual doctors and/or mounting fiscal pressure on hospitals or insurers to reverse this trend.

Recent case law

One case which reached the Court of Appeal in this country some years ago [1] is of interest because it is the first time that a British court, or to be precise, an English court, acknowledged and condoned that some infants should be allowed to die instead of being treated aggressively to save their lives at all costs. The case reached the courts, not because the paediatricians were opting out of their responsibility to take decisions, but because the baby, who had multiple problems including a brain defect, had earlier been made a ward of court by the social services department on the grounds that the parents could not care for her properly. When the time came for difficult questions and decisions about what life-saving interventions were appropriate if the baby became infected or otherwise seriously ill, the paediatricians disagreed with the social services department about the appropriate course of action. At the lower court Mr. Justice Ward was satisfied that the baby would be permanently unable to interact mentally, physically and socially and ordered:

1. That the hospital authority be at liberty 'to treat the minor to die'.
2. That they should administer such treatment as might relieve her from pain, suffering and distress but that it should not be necessary to administer antibiotics to treat any serious infection or set up intravenous infusions or nasogastric feeding.

3. That the hospital authority continue to treat the baby as outlined in a report commissioned by the Official Solicitor from an independent paediatrician. In this report the paediatrician had not ruled out the administration of antibiotics, intravenous infusions or gastric feeding as long as they were to achieve the primary object of relieving pain, suffering and distress.

The case reached the Court of Appeal because the Official Solicitor appealed to Justice Ward's directions on two counts:

1. His order 3, i.e. to use antibiotics, intravenous infusions or gastric feeding to relieve, pain, suffering and distress contradicted his order number 2, i.e. that it should not be necessary to use these procedures. Paediatricians considered that these are judgements which should be made by them and not by the court.
2. More importantly, however, the Official Solicitor took exception to the order to 'treat the minor to die' as this was capable of being misunderstood. Contrary to some initial impressions it did *not* authorize active intervention to cause the infant's death.

Justice Ward accordingly reworded his phrase to indicate that the Health Authority should be at liberty 'to treat the baby to come to an end peacefully and with dignity'.

In a commentary, Derek Morgan points out that this case does not tell us, nor does it purport to do so, what other cases of severe disability might be included in such a verdict. In 1981 *In Re B* [2] the court indicate`d that it could envisage an infant whose life 'is demonstrably going to be so awful that in effect the child must be condemned to die'.

Morgan also pointed out that this recent case demonstrates that courts are not blessed with any particular expertise in these cases. He quotes Justice La Forrest, from the Supreme Court of Canada, in a different but related case: 'judges are generally ill informed about many of the factors relevant to a wise decision in this difficult area ..... however well presented a case may be, it can only partially inform'. Unfortunately too, this kind of court process inevitably means a delay in reaching a decision while the indignity or offence to the neonate may be compounded (Morgan 1989).

Bioethics Committees

In attempts to defuse the confrontation between paediatricians and government precipitated by the Baby Doe Rules, it was suggested by the American Academy of Pediatrics and others that committees be set up to review non-treatment decisions. A model already existed since the early seventies to deal with DNR (do not resuscitate) decisions and other issues affecting the elderly. Infant Care Review Committees (ICRC) or Infant Ethics Committees (IEC) have a broad interdisciplinary and lay membership and a wide remit to review cases, to recommend policies and practices within the hospital, and to educate. Good committees attempt to clarify the medical and ethical issues and provide extra assurance that the infant's best interests have been properly considered. As Fleischman has observed they may also provide some ethical 'comfort' for the doctors and staff who have to struggle with these complex problems (Fleischman 1986). In particular their role should be advisory - committees like these should not make decisions, but can recommend that particularly difficult problems be referred to the courts. Unfortunately, in the current climate of legislative interference and with the increasing tendency to resort to litigation to solve medical disputes, in some hospitals the ethics committees have taken on, or have been seen to take on, a decision-making role and many doctors, understandably, have been only too happy to 'pass the buck' of difficult decision-making to a committee. As they, the committees, are institutionally based, and may contain lawyers and hospital administrators as members, their decisions may have less to do with the welfare of the infant and family than the interests of the institution. Perhaps even worse, as I learned in one hospital, when *no* decision is taken the situation is allowed to 'drift' - to nobody's benefit. The parents, in spite of the fact that they are the ones most affected, may have relatively little part in the discussions.

In this country we have not yet formalized such a committee structure although there is often wide consultation with individuals similar to those in the American committees. They include specialist colleagues, nurses, social workers, and clergymen but not lay persons outside the family, hospital administrators or lawyers. It seems to me that infant ethics committees properly constituted can serve a useful purpose in guiding the medical staff towards decisions that are sound in ethics as well as in medicine, but I fear the stultifying mini-bureaucracies they may create within hospitals and I remain sceptical that most committees, as currently constituted, will improve the quality of prospective decision-making in individual cases.

Lawyers have criticized lack of due process in decisions to allow infants to die and what they see as the medical professions's unwillingness to establish rules of conduct. Rules imply rigidity. Individual doctors have suggested guidelines or criteria for such decisions but have emphasized the importance of flexibility and pointed out that as the individual circumstances are so varied much latitude in decision making should be expected and tolerated. Paediatricians working in neonatal units have widely varying personal views on the appropriate use of intensive care. How selectively or how indiscriminately they use their skills and technology will be the subject of continuing debate both inside and outside these units. Inevitably the criteria will continue to change but we must remain sensitive to the effects of treatment policies on the infants themselves and the families who must bear the consequences. I believe that it would be folly to remove the responsibility, the obligation, the duty and the agony of final decision making from the doctors primarily responsible for the case of patients and the appropriate next of kin, in this case the parents. In an increasingly pluralistic society there should be room for discretion based not only on medical and technical considerations but on personal, religious and cultural values as they affect and are cherished by individual families.

Notes

1. *In Re C* [1989] 2 ALL ER 782, CA.
2. *In Re B* [1981] 1 WLR 1421, CA.

12 Against killing the patient

Jennifer Jackson

Among doctors in this country and in the U.S.A. there is a widespread consensus in support of the view that while it is always wrong to kill a patient intentionally it is sometimes permissible to let a patient die. The same consensus is not to be found amoung philosophers, many of whom are highly critical of this view. First of all, they do not agree that killing patients is always wrong. But secondly, they contend that the view not only smooths over the harsh implications of this unconditional prohibition in practice, but cannot really be defended at the level of theory.

In what follows I will defend the consensus view against these criticisms. Non-philosophers who defend the consensus view may not be unduly troubled if this distinction to which they subscribe, though intuitively appealing, is 'logically' hard to justify.[1] As a philosopher I must take the charge of illogicality or inconsistency more seriously. The importance of clear thinking in this area can hardly be exaggerated. So I make no apology for raising issues which have had considerable attention already. There is more to be said - especially on the side of those who uphold the distinction -

philosophical *defences* in recent times are relatively scarce.

The traditional teaching

In order to make sense of the attitude of many doctors we need to examine what I shall call the 'traditional teaching' which underlies it. Two caveats about this label: 1) In calling this teaching 'traditional' I would not wish to prejudice readers either for or against it. A teaching which boasts a long history may reflect the wisdom of our ancestors or merely their long-standing prejudices and muddled thinking. 2) I lay no claim to historical accuracy, though I believe that the view I describe as 'traditional' captures a central aspect of what many moralists have wanted to say.

According to this traditional teaching it is always impermissible to intend, i.e. to aim at, an innocent person's death either as a means to what one seeks to accomplish or as itself what one is seeking to accomplish. But it is sometimes permissible to cause an innocent person's death where that is simply a consequence foreseen and accepted of what one is trying to accomplish, a mere by-product of one's aim and incidental to it.[2]

An agent, is, of course, causally responsible both for the intended and the foreseen consequences of his actions. But causal responsibility is not the same as moral responsibility. In some cases, not all, an agent may be blameless for bringing about a consequence merely foreseen where he would be blameworthy were that consequence intended. What the agent does is the same, yields precisely the same result. Yet in one case his action may be innocent, in the other not.

Compare, for example: 1) A buys the last cake in the bakery foreseeing that B, next in the queue, must in consequence go without. 2) A buys the last cake in the bakery in order spitefully to deprive B who is next in line. In both cases A deprives B knowingly, but only in the latter case must A be blameworthy. (I am of course assuming, for the sake of argument, that it is within one's rights and not necessarily a 'mean' act to buy a cake, even the last, but not within one's right to act maliciously).

Emphatically, it is not here being suggested that one is never blameworthy for consequences merely foreseen. Suppose, for example, 3) A helps himself to two portions of cake at a dinner party foreseeing, though not aiming to secure, that other guests in consequence will not get any. (I am here assuming that being served ahead of other guests at the dinner table does not entitle one to behave as if one were at the head of a queue).

The distinction between bringing about someone's death as an intended consequence or as a merely foreseen (but unintended) consequence of what one does is not to be confused with that between causing someone's death by action or by inaction - in this respect expressing the distinction at issue as between the active sounding 'killing' and the passive sounding 'allowing to die' is misleading. Someone else's death may be only a foreseen consequence equally where the causally responsible agent decides to do or decides not to do: as when the agent decides to switch off, or not to switch on, a respirator merely to save electricity and without the least concern for a patient dependent on it (a fanciful example one hopes, but that is beside the point). Likewise someone else's death may be intended as much by a decision not to act as by a decision to act (as much by withholding life-saving treatment as by administering a lethal injection).

In other words, things that result from your doings may not be intended and things that result from your not-doings may be intended. The first of these points seems too obvious to labour. The second, though, might not carry immediate conviction; that the results of your not-doings can be intended.

There are two points to be clarified:

1. that not-doings can have consequences,
2. that consequences of not-doings can count as intended.

Not-doings can have consequences. It might seem that a not-doing is the mere absence of a cause and that only causes have effects i.e. consequences. But it is easy to see that we can bring something about by failing to intervene in an ongoing process. There is anyway a degree of arbitrariness as to whether we cast our account of what happens in a positive or negative mode and also as to whether we perceive an act to be positive or negative - which, for example, is 'slimming' or 'keeping a secret' or, indeed, 'nursing care only': a doing or a not-doing?

Those defenders of the traditional teaching who attach a significance to whether a patient's death is achieved by a doing or a not-doing want to include in the category of not-doings not only withholding of treatment but withdrawings. Now to be sure a decision to withdraw is a decision not-to-continue-to-do but is it not also inescapably a decision to do (as a means to not-continuing-to-do)? Whereas a consultant who fails to attempt resuscitation can truthfully say 'I did nothing', the consultant who turns off and disconnects cannot truthfully say 'I did nothing' though (as I hope to show) he might be justified in saying 'I did nothing wrong'. If, on the other hand, defenders of the traditional teaching concede that withdrawing is a doing yet insist on attaching critical significance to whether a patient's death is achieved by a doing or a not-doing, the implications of their interpretation of the traditional teaching will indeed be harsh.

At any rate even where subjects have uncontroversially *not* acted, we may be able to identify some of the consequences of their not-doings. The not-doings which concern us here are omissions or failures, as these often reveal why on a given occasion the unexpected happens. Where we are interested to know why something has happened which normally does not, we cast around among the necessary conditions and select from that set as the 'cause' some departure, deviation, some abnormal condition which explains why on this occasion things have turned out differently. In this way a guardsman's failure to signal is deemed the cause of a collision, a gardener's failure to water flowers, the cause of their dying or, indeed, a doctor's failure to administer penicillin, the cause of his patient's death.[3]

Since, as we have noted, the distinction between doings and not-doings is often indeterminate and since anyway the distinction between consequences intended and merely foreseen is quite independent of it, we will assume that the adequacy of the traditional teaching depends only on the credibility of attaching moral significance to this latter distinction. The implications of this traditional teaching, as applied to doctoring, are that while there are some circumstances in which a doctor might be justified in deciding to permit a patient to die whether by withholding or withdrawing life-saving treatment, there are no circumstances in which a doctor might be justified in aiming at a patient's death whether by withholding or withdrawing life-saving treatment.

When letting die is not a breach of duty

In what kind of circumstance might a doctor be justified in deciding to let a patient die? Discounting scarce resources, there are two obvious grounds for withholding (or withdrawing) life-saving treatment, neither of which is ruled out by the traditional teaching - (1) the patient refuses it; and (2) it is not of net benefit to the patient.[4]

To be sure in the second kind of case the doctor probably believes that the patient would be 'better off' dead and hence the doctor may even hope that death comes quickly. It does not follow that by withholding life-saving treatment the doctor is trying to kill that patient. Rather the doctor may simply be unwilling to do anything to arrest the patient's dying where so doing would clearly be of no benefit to the patient e.g. refusing to insert a nasal-gastric tube in a patient no longer able to swallow food.

Prima facie a doctor who decides to let a patient die acts indefensibly: he fails in his duty of care. But the doctor's duty of care does not commit him to saving a patient's life come what may. In some circumstances it is consistent with his duty of care to let die; in some circumstances, he may even be obliged (through that very duty, not just by some other overriding duty) so to do.

Granted that the doctor's duty of care commits him to regarding the patient's interests as the governing consideration in the light of which treatment decisions are to be made, how much care is he obliged to render to a particular patient? It cannot be that his duty to a particular patient requires him to do everything he can for the patient's benefit: there are other patients with a claim on his attention, and other non-medical claims on him too, no doubt - e.g. family. Moreover is he not entitled to time off from the round of duty-fulfilling activities?

Legally, the extent and nature of his obligation is judged in the light of 'good medical practice' - by which we are to understand, whatever practice prevails among reputable practitioners. Of course, we may regard the legal definition of duty as demarcating merely the bottom line: a doctor ought to do more for his patient than just what the law requires of him.

Yet suppose a doctor deviates from standard practice in his caring endeavours as follows: it is said to be common medical practice 'to allow an anencephalic baby, or one with trisomy-18, to die by providing only comfort, water and sedation'.[5] Suppose a doctor puts one such baby on a respirator, starts intravenous or gastric feedings, and administers medications to prevent circulatory collapse, or interferes with the process of dying by resuscitation. Is not this doctor, in deviating from the standard practice, doing more than the law requires by way of caring, acting above and beyond the call of duty? No. He does more to the patient but not for the patient. He acts against the baby's interests. In short, the duty of care may oblige a doctor to withhold or withdraw available life-saving treatment. Even the provision of nourishment in some situations can become contrary to a patient's interests, in which case imposing it would be inconsistent with caring.[6]

Normally, it is in a patient's interests to receive whatever treatment is of net benefit to his health. But suppose it should happen otherwise. Suppose a patient who has acute appendicitis also happens to be under sentence of death and his appeal has been rejected. In such a case doctors could expect by surgery to restore the patient to good health but how could that be in the patient's interests? Yet where it is clearly not in the patient's interest to undergo a treatment, one would expect the patient to withhold consent and doctors are obliged not to override the refusal of consent from a competent patient. And if the patient were not himself competent to refuse, proxy consent would be needed and the proxy would be obliged to act on the patient's behalf - he too presumably should refuse.

When is a killing intentional?

It may be argued that an account of intentionality which restricts the scope of your intention just to ends aimed at and means chosen to bring about those ends (you aim at the end via aiming at the means) has only a surface plausibility. One might ask: if you choose to do X as your means and in doing X you are doing Y does it follow that since X-ing is intentional, so is Y-ing? Obviously not. For one thing, no one would want to say that your Y-ing is intentional unless at least you know that you are Y-ing. Even then, it may not be true that your Y-ing is intentional; as Elizabeth Anscombe pointed out years ago, what you do may be intentional under one description and not under another.[7] You are, for example, rummaging in a drawer looking for a mislaid key which you urgently need. By so doing, perhaps, you are messing up a drawer you have just tidied. Now the rummaging must be intentional - it has a point. But not the messing - this you do neither with any end in view nor for its own sake.

It is worth pointing out that where you are aware that in X-ing you are Y-ing, the fact that you are Y-ing may be unwelcome to you without affecting Y's status in respect of intention. Thus it does not suffice to establish that your Y-ing is non-intentional merely that you deem it regrettable. Sometimes, after all, your chosen means is pursued regretfully, but intentionally nonetheless.

While the foregoing observations about intentional doings have a certain plausibility, their ethical implications appear to be disconcerting. Suppose a doctor undertakes to remove some vital organs from a terminally-ill patient. He proposes, let us say, to transfer the patient's heart to one person, his liver to another. Now the question whether the end justifies the means does not arise if that means is unconditionally prohibited. But what *is* the means in this case? Granted that the doctor intentionally removes vital organs knowing (since neither he nor anyone else plans to replace them) that in so doing he is killing his patient, does it follow that this killing is a means?

We have noted that mere regret over doing Y is not sufficient to establish that you do it non-intentionally. But by analogy with our earlier example (of the non-intentional messing of a drawer) it would seem that we must allow that the doctor's killing need not be (and is unlikely to be) intentional. The answer to why he is killing his patient may be that so doing serves no end of his; his aim even as a means cannot be so described and if the patient were miraculously to arise organless from his bed saying 'Good afternoon, Doctor' the doctor would be quite delighted.

And yet, how could a doctor who acted thus credibly protest: 'But I never intended to kill the patient'? Not only is this narrow construction of the scope of intention in what one does out of line with what it seems natural to say but it marginalizes and makes a mockery of the constraint on killing. It would entitle a thief who kills to say truthfully that his only aim is to silence his victims by cutting their throats, their deaths being incidental to his purpose.

We need it seems to widen the scope of intention to include besides the ends aimed at and the means chosen also any consequence or side-effect which is seen to be essentially bound up with the type of action which is one's chosen means. If it is known that X-ing is always inevitably Y-ing, then the Y-ing is intentional. But if the X-ing just happens in the circumstances in question necessarily to involve Y-ing and the agent fully realizes this, the Y-ing need not be intended. Thus messing up a drawer is not inevitably part of searching in it for something mislaid - the drawer may be messy already. But carving up a patient or cutting someone's throat is inevitably killing the person. To be sure if one considers the kinds of situation in which a doctor might be tempted to withdraw or withhold life-saving treatment, e.g. to switch off a respirator or to dismantle intravenous feeding, it may be dead certain that the patient will die in consequence. But neither *type* of action is inevitably bound up with ending a patient's life. Thus the death though foreseen and allowed may still be properly deemed to be incidental to the doctor's purpose.

The practice: its alleged inhumanity

Situations in which doctors who subscribe to the teaching are prevented by it from acting humanely are, I suspect, very unusual. Many cases cited as supportive of euthanasia are not instances of euthanasia i.e. intentional killing, at all. The teaching allows a doctor to decide on whatever course of treatment is consistent with the duty of care, be it initiating, withholding or withdrawing life-saving treatment, provided only that the *aim* of the treatment is not: to kill.

Yet it may be argued that if doctors who subscribe to the teaching are rarely prevented by it from acting humanely that is only because they anticipate the dilemma to which their teaching would expose them if they did not take suitable precautions. The suitable precautions involve not doing all that one might to sustain a precarious life lest the patient survive indefinitely in a severely incapacitated state e.g. permanently comatose. John Freeman describes various types of predicament where doctors are disposed to 'make less than a full initial effort because they think the outlook for "good" recovery is small'. 'How often', he asks 'do we find that we later regret that "we did everything" when we see the patient remain unresponsive or severely impaired and resolve next time we will do less and avoid disaster?'.[8] Thus, it might appear that if only doctors were to repudiate the traditional teaching and euthanasia were legalized, more lives would be saved.

But why should a doctor's decision to initiate life-saving treatment jeopardize his freedom at a later stage to withdraw it? Freeman observes that at the later stage if the outcome is 'bad' passive euthanasia may not work - the patient may survive. But of course subscribers to the teaching are not in favour of passive euthanasia, of trying to kill by withdrawing treatment. What they can allow, though, is withdrawal of treatment and of normal forms of care which in a given case are of no benefit to the patient and which if withdrawn render death a certain (yet not intended) consequence. Proper care, then, for patients for whom 'everything' has been done but who turn out to be hopeless cases may involve no more than the relief of discomfort. Would patients treated so die lingering deaths or live on indefinitely in a comatose state?

To be sure there will be times when kindly and concerned doctors who accept the teaching will be distressed that it does not permit them to commit murder; times when killing would (obviously) be merciful. It does not follow that sticking to the rule in such circumstances is 'inhumane'; 'inhumane' implies not just 'allowing suffering' but 'allowing pointless suffering'. If the teaching is sound, then following it is not pointless. But that is not to say that the individual suffering patient must somehow (in some unobvious and roundabout way) be better off because his doctor follows the rule. No one supposes that a doctor must be 'kind' or 'humane' come what may. Nor is a doctor to be accused of unkindness or inhumanity just because he refuses to lie, to swindle, to murder etc.

One kind of case where caring doctors could spare infants distress if only murder were permissible would seem to be with incidents of the severe dermatological affliction, epidermolysis bullosa, a congenital disorder which causes widespread and constant blistering of the skin and multiple lesions both on the body surface and on skin within the body. There is no cure. Infants who may survive with this disorder up to a year or two suffer pain every time they are handled and they need frequent handling: several bandage changes daily, infections treated, intravenous feeding. Often there are further complications associated with the disease and requiring painful treatment e.g. an intestinal obstruction requiring surgery.[9]

In such a case a decision by all concerned not to 'prolong life' may readily be reached. But thereafter, waiting for 'nature to take its course', even if that takes a few days only, is not in the *infant's* best interests. Thus those who hold to the strict rule against killing must ground it otherwise.

The philosophy behind the theory

Granted that some line-drawing teaching is necessary, i.e. doctors should sometimes decide against a life-saving treatment and some rule or guidance is needed as a basis for making such decisions, why select this particular teaching?

Might not a straightforwardly beneficent directive (or a beneficent directive suitably modified to accommodate respect for patient autonomy) be preferable: 'Decide (where possible, in consultation with the patient) according to what seems best for the patient'?

Helga Kuhse claims that what underlies the traditional teaching is the 'Sanctity of Life Ideal according to which human life is both inviolable and valuable'.[10] Supporters of the teaching if they are wise, though, will not talk of any such ideal but of an imperative, a prohibition we must (hence, can) obey, not a goal we are urged to strive after as best we can.

As for the alleged 'inviolability' and 'valuableness' of human life, these seem most unpromising bases on which to ground the teaching. What after all is it to assert the inviolability of human life other than to assert the wrongness of killing? Asserting the wrongness of killing hardly helps us towards an understanding of the rightness of letting die. As for the valuableness of human life, it is far from clear what such an assertion amounts to or implies, still less how acknowledging said value reveals the necessity of a strict prohibition on taking lives but not on letting die.

But the strict prohibition on *taking* human life may be made sense of without appeal to the idea that human life is sacred, incomparably precious, and death the worst outcome for any patient. Rather than base the teaching on the mere assertion, unsupported by theological underpinning, that human life has infinite value,[11] I would defend it as a teaching which is *socially* necessary, insofar as communal life becomes precarious unless a strict rule against taking human life is generally and effectively taught, upheld, respected and enforced.[12]

Whereas a moral teaching against taking human life is a social necessity, the same is not true in regard to saving life. A community may be perfectly viable though its members are not brought up to believe that there is a general duty upon everyone to do all that one can to preserve human life. It stands to reason, though, that in any community there will be certain people who assume a special duty to preserve other people's lives in situations of danger - police, firemen, life-guards, doctors. But *their* duties towards those at risk are not unlimited - not even if they are committed to ideals of service as part of their vocation or calling. To be sure, doctors who refrain from giving life-saving treatment are causally responsible for their patients' deaths, and since they have a special duty of care and care normally requires providing the necessaries of life, they have to answer for their decisions to let die. Yet there are occasions when such decisions are morally defensible: the duty of care does not necessitate forcing life-saving treatment on a unwilling recipient, nor does it necessitate life-saving treatment in the unusual circumstances that this is of no benefit to the recipient. Thus the teaching can at least be made sense of which strictly prohibits everyone, doctors included, from taking life but does not oblige everyone, not even doctors, to save life wherever possible.

Concluding remarks

The foregoing discussion constitutes only a limited defence of the consensus view. I have attempted to defend that view just against these two charges: (1) that the distinction on which it rests cannot be given an intelligible basis and (2) that it commits its followers to inhumane practices. The view may, of course, be open to other charges: e.g. an intelligible basis may still be inadequate in that it relies on false or doubtful assumptions.

Here I have suggested that a secular defence of the strict rule against intentional killing as opposed to decisions to allow to die should be based on an understanding of what moral teaching any human community needs to adopt and uphold as an essential underpinning to peaceful co-existence in it.

The supposition that such a teaching is socially necessary may be disputed: it is not obvious - at any rate, not obviously obvious. Indeed a radical sceptic may observe that since the intentional killing of 'innocent' humans is endemic throughout human history, the idea that a strict rule against it is 'socially necessary' is just laughable. But though I admit that such killings have been commonplace, tolerance of them, I suggest, has not been. A moral teaching may be effective enough if it is taken seriously by most people and the fact that people fail to follow it does not necessarily show that they dismiss it. But insofar as we do become generally complacent about intentional killing, we put civilization at risk: I am not here thinking of the risk posed by modern powerful weaponry but of the risk that has always obtained, that Hobbes recognized, the danger that arises if people cease to be able to trust one another not to act murderously. For all that murder may be commonplace, I do not think we have yet reached that point.

A moderate sceptic, while accepting the social necessity of a pretty strict teaching against killing may still demur at the rigidity of the traditional teaching – it accommodates some compromise in allowing that the taking of non-innocent life may be justified but it refuses to consider further possible qualifications. Have we good reason to believe that a more qualified teaching, permitting intentional killing in certain specified circumstances, would not suffice?

Even if any relaxation of the strict teaching would carry risks, some might say that those risks are worth taking. To be sure we might in consequence find ourselves sliding down a slippery slope. But sliding down a slope is not falling over a cliff: it may be possible to arrest our descent before we slide too far. And, especially if we are a little unsure of our inherited present footing, we might reasonably proceed with caution rather than refuse to budge.

All the same, if, as I have argued, the consensus view can be given an intelligible basis and is not inhumane in its implications, it does at least deserve further consideration, especially as it is a view which finds favour with many of the medical practitioners who are involved in making life and death decisions.

Some people, though, are found to protest at all this 'philosophizing' on behalf of the consensus view. In their view it is a time-wasting irrelevance: ethics is about caring, is it not? Does a good (caring) doctor have need of ethical rules – other than the basic Golden Rule, 'Do unto others ...'? In what way is the traditional teaching which underlies the consensus view superior to a simple beneficent teaching, 'Do whatever is best for the patient'?

A society which taught beneficence unchecked by the constraints of justice would be unnervingly insecure. For your conscientious caring doctor, in such a society, everything would be permitted if intended for your good - he could betray your confidences, lie to you or, of course, kill you. Is it not safer to have a teaching that the constraints of justice are to act as checks on how we all treat each other no matter how noble or ignoble our intentions? Is that not the thrust of the maxim oft cited as trumping a doctor's duty to put his patients' interests first: 'Above all do no harm'? That is why patients' interests are on the whole better served if doctors follow the traditional teaching rather than a more overtly beneficent teaching.

Notes

1. 'Thus we are guilty of inconsistency but not of infanticide' says J.K. Mason (1988), p. 116. Mason, in defending selective neo-natal treatment, champions the consensus view. He argues that it is necessary to make a stand against killing, as opposed to letting die, in order to avoid the hazards of standing on a slippery slope (p.57). But since he equates letting die with passive euthanasia (p. 23; 61), I would argue that his choice of perch is arbitrary: if the slope really is slippery, he is already sliding.
2. There is nothing erudite in this distinction on which the traditional teaching relies between consequences intended and foreseen. As Anthony Kenny observes:

> it is not usually natural to speak of someone as intending foreseen consequences of his action when these are unwanted or when he is merely indifferent to them .... Many people drink too much knowing that they will suffer a hangover, and eat too much knowing that they will put on weight: but they don't drink *in order to* produce a hangover or eat with the intention of putting on weight.

In legal contexts, though, as Kenny remarks, intention is sometimes interpreted more widely to include consequences merely foreseen - though even then the same distinction tends to crop up, redrawn in terms of what is merely obliquely intended as against what is directly intended. (Kenny 1978, p. 50.).

3. Cf. Hart and Honore (1959), pp. 28-29. Note that omissions only become causes where what is omitted is a deviation from the normal. See Helga Kuhse's criticisms of the Hart and Honore account (1987), pp 54ff.
4. Cf. Bonnie Steinbock, 'The intentional termination of life', in her (1980). I discuss these grounds in 'Withholding neonatal care' in Bromham, Dalton and Jackson, (eds) (1990).
5. See Shaw, (1987), p.126.
6. Cf. A.G.M. Campbell's paper 'Neonatal intensive care: where and how to draw the line', in this volume.
7. Anscombe (1957), s.6.
8. McMillan R. *et al.* (1987), p. 159.
9. See Shelp, 'Choosing Among Evils' in McMillan R. *et al.*, *op.cit.*, p. 225. Cf. Frohock (1986), p. 26ff.
10. Kuhse (1984), p.26.
11. Cf. Kuhse (1987), p. 13. The BMA Working Party on Euthanasia, while acknowledging that the religious conviction which formerly underlay the concept of sanctity of life is 'no longer a universally accepted basis for medical practice' observes that:

> A recognition of the sanctity of human life (while not explicitly religious in nature) recognises that any presumption on the part of doctors, to do as and what they may choose to the lives of persons, undermines the value of mutual humanity and reverence and respect felt when we confront the most profound aspects of life. (BMA Working Party 1988, p. 41).

This observation constitutes an argument for recognizing the sanctity of life non-religiously only if it is credible to maintain that only those who do so avoid the presumption that, as doctors, they can do as and what they may choose to the lives of persons. It is *not* credible.

12. Actually, of course, the teaching is qualified against the taking of innocent human life. And rightly so, since a teaching which forbade self-defence against murderous assault would be unrealistically severe; it could not be taken seriously. Admittedly, there are some, the Jains, who successfully follow a teaching which is even more severe, forbidding the taking of life, human or non-human, but I submit that they are able to do so only because they are cushioned by a society which follows a more qualified rule. About the Jains see James Rachels (1986), pp. 20ff.

13 Reactive and objective attitudes in psychiatry

Grant Gillett

> The future accumulates like a weight upon the past. The weight upon the earliest years is easier to remove to let that time spring up like grass that has been crushed. The years following childhood become welded to their future, massed like stone, and often the time beneath cannot spring back into growth like new grass: it lies bled of its green in a new shape with those frail bloodless sprouts of another, unfamiliar time, entangled one with the other beneath the stone.[1]

Our futures are built upon our pasts in the sense that, from inchoate and multipotential beginnings, our mental life congeals into forms that are resistant to change. For most of us these forms are comfortable, they move with us, accommodating our desires and beliefs so as to offer ready *personae* which can adapt to the demands of everyday situations and express who we are. For most of us the valleys, mountains, hiding places, cobbled streets and familiar haunts of self and personality are human constructions adequate to cope with adult experience, but for some, a few, the forms that congeal are oppressive, entrapping, they alienate one's *personae* from oneself. For yet others the process or actuality of life and thought are fractured and disrupted by the intrusion of absurd and apparently malign influences. Human beings in such predicaments are psychologically disturbed. As a result, our reactions to them and their reactions to us have none of the familiar reciprocity that characterizes our relationships to normal people. We base certain attitudes on our reactions to the intentions we discern in the behaviour of others and these reactive attitudes structure our life together as persons. But they go awry with 'strange' folk whom we are forced to look at as being 'other' than we are. Therefore we adopt attitudes which treat them, to some extent, as malfunctioning systems or objects (albeit of immense complexity and unpredictability), as the focus of objective rather than reactive attitudes.

> I had seen in the ward office the list of those 'down for a leucotomy', with my name on the list, and other names being crossed off as the operation was performed. My 'turn' must have been very close when one evening the superintendent of the hospital, Dr. Blake Palmer, made an unusual visit to the ward. He spoke to me – to the amazement of everyone.
> As it was my first chance to discuss with anyone, apart from those who had persuaded me, the prospect of my operation, I said urgently, 'Dr. Blake Palmer, what do you think?' He pointed to the newspaper in his hand. 'About the prize?'
> I was bewildered. What prize? 'No', I said, 'about the leucotomy'.
> He looked stern, 'I've decided that you should stay as you are. I don't want you changed'..
> 'You've won the Hubert Church Award for the best prose. Your book, *The Lagoon*' ...
> I smiled 'Have I?'
> 'Yes. And we're moving you out of this ward. And no leucotomy'.
> The winning of the prize and the attention of a new doctor from Scotland who accepted me as I appeared to him and not as he learned about me from my 'history' or reports of me ... enabled me to be prepared for discharge from hospital. Instead of being treated by leucotomy, I was treated as a person of some worth, a human

> being, in spite of the misgivings and unwillingness of some members of the staff.[2]

This passage starkly paints the contrast between objective and reactive attitudes. On the one hand there are attitudes which negate the personality and thoughts of the patient - 'He spoke to me - to the amazement of everyone', '*I've decided* that you should stay as you are', '*we're moving* you out of this ward'. On the other hand there are reactive attitudes evinced in other interactions - 'who accepted me as I appeared to him', 'I was treated as a person of some worth'. These attitudes jostle one another for space in psychiatric practice and we must unpack them in order to understand how they can be reconciled. To that end we need to explore the thoughts involved, their role in our understanding of persons, the situations in which reactive attitudes are suspended and the dangers therein, their role and importance in the construction of a self or personal identity and their relation to current psychiatric theory and practice.

I. Reactive attitudes and the self as thinker

Sir Peter Strawson has outlined the nature of reactive and objective attitudes with an elegance and economy of style that I can emulate but not hope to match.

> We should think of the many different kinds of relationship which we can have with other people - as sharers of a common interest; as members of the same family; as colleagues; as friends; as lovers; as chance parties to an enormous range of transactions and encounters. Then we should think, in each of these connections in turn, and in others, of the kind of importance we attach to the attitudes and intentions towards us of those who stand in these relationships to us, and of the kinds of reactive attitudes to which we ourselves are prone.[3]
> What I want to contrast is the attitude (or range of attitudes) of involvement or participation on the one hand, and what might be called the objective attitude (or range of attitudes) to another human being, on the other. Even in the same situation, I must add, they are

> not exclusive of each other; but they are, profoundly, opposed to each other.[4]
>
> Exceptionally, I have said, we can have direct dealings with other human beings without any degree of personal involvement, treating them simply as creatures to be handled in our own interests, or our side's, or society's - or even theirs. In the extreme case of the mentally deranged, it is easy to see the connection between the possibility of a wholly objective attitude and the impossibility of what we understand by ordinary inter-personal relationships.[5]

In these passages Strawson identifies a deep tension in our attitudes in general which is of sharp relevance to those who practise psychiatry. In their communications to their patients they are naturally inclined to develop reactive attitudes to them but on the other they must treat these same individuals as cases to be managed.

In forming and manifesting reactive attitudes one engages with another person, expecting to find there a certain reciprocity toward oneself. In such reciprocal engagement the thoughts and reactions of the other are incorporated into the attitudes one develops. In fact the other person has a dual role; she serves both as a proper object of reactive attitudes and as a source for validation of one's own attitudes. Objective attitudes are quite different: they detach one from the other person and incline one not to look *to* her to find guidance in shaping the relationship and an understanding of her behaviour but rather to look *at* her as a locus of phenomena to be analyzed according to a less interactive set of thoughts. This observational stance, in effect, negates the effect on oneself of the other as a person.

Karl Jaspers hints at a similar fundamental distinction between what can be learned about a patient fromn 'empathic experience' and what can be discerned as 'evidence based on the principle of causality'.[6] He says of the scientific and detached view 'as objective psychology .. it is capable of reaching extraordinarily exact results but by the same token, by its very nature, it never can give an answer to the question of phenomenology and of the psychology of meaning'.[7] Both Strawson and Jaspers link an understanding of the person and her intentions, which are framed in terms of what means something to her, to a different kind of discourse from that involved in objective attitudes toward and explanations of what a human being does. The former discourse is *empathic* and the latter *detached* with respect to the perspective of the individual under consideration.

The tension between these two modes of appreciation is made even clearer when we explore their epistemological properties. In reactive attitudes one discerns the thoughts or intentions of another person by liberal use of a principle of charity according to a norm of rationality. I.e. one makes sense of another person's behaviour by assuming that she generally believes what is true and is inclined to want what is good.[8] On this basis we establish communication and thereby the mutual understanding that fosters the development of reciprocity; if we abandon these epistemological foundations our understanding of the other person rapidly evaporates. For instance, imagine the following conversation:

'Stop here! This is where I get off'.
'But you can't get off, we're in an aeroplane'.
'Are you crazy! I'm hitchhiking and I don't want to go any further!'
'Look, I think I'd better call the hostess'

Or the following:

'I want that'.
'You what?'
'I want that to eat with tomato sauce'
'But it's a rock'
'I know, that's why I'm not having cream with it'.

In both cases what we have heard is insane, we cannot make rational sense of it. Because we cannot share the perspectives of the subjects involved we cannot chart the structure of their thinking. It is not far from such cases, where our empathy fails, to the 'moral insanity' that Strawson concerns himself with in discussing freedom and responsibility.

> ...we see the agent in a different light: as one whose picture of the world is an insane delusion; or as one whose behaviour, or part of whose behaviour, is unintelligible to us, perhaps even to him, in terms of conscious purposes, and intelligible only in terms of unconscious purposes; or even perhaps, as one wholly impervious to the self-reactive attitudes I spoke of. Seeing an agent in such a light as this tends ... to inhibit ordinary inter-personal attitudes in general, and the kind of demand and expectation which those atitudes involve; and tends to promote instead the purely objective view of the agent as one posing problems simply of intellectual understanding, management, treatment and control.[9]

Where we detach from the agents concerned, suspending the principle of charity and the reciprocity that flows from it, we have trouble making sense of the behaviour concerned and thus we have trouble knowing how to react to what is going on. This, of course, implies that assignments of praise or blame or their legal extensions become insecure where we are forced into a non-empathic mode in our attempts to understand a person's actions.

Our reactive attitudes are based on the perceived intentions and attitudes of others. In the problem cases these do not hang together in the normal way and the currency of discourse in which we recognize our affinity with others and develop relationships is unusable. But such discourse is the milieu in which human beings articulate and develop their thoughts and thus the fundamental ground not only for one's dealings with others but also for the understanding of self as a thinking subject. Just as I appreciate others as persons by empathic experience, so I learn what-it-is-like-to-be-a-person, i.e. how to find my way about in my own experience according to the concepts I share with others. For instance, I learn what counts as being hurt, for creatures who are like me, when I can organise my thinking about what is happening to me and others with this key concept (and many others like it) in place. It is natural that reactive attitudes should have explanatory, communicative and formative roles of this type in a thinker's mental life, because mental ascriptions, which are the currency of mental explanation, communication and the formation of self, are taught and learnt in interpersonal exchanges. Empathic experiences of the reactions of others, which depend on my communicating with them and appreciating what they say, also provide me with the techniques of self-reflection and self-mastery. For example, if I ask my father why he shouted at my mother then he could react in various ways. He might evince resentment and rejection of my attempt to understand his activity or, alternatively, try to unpack and explain his own reactions, including me in the reflective process of self-scrutiny. On the other hand, it is likely that if he tends to react negatively to such an exchange then I myself will have problems with anger and not achieve a reflective mastery over my emotions. His reactive attitudes, based on his perception that my question was threatening him in some sense, are not conducive to constructive activity in such a situation. If he says something like 'Mind your own business!' or 'So you're on her side as well!' I will read situations which call forth such reactive tendencies in myself differently from the way that I would if he were to act with more sensitivity. I may not have had the hostile intentions he imputes to me but his reactions and the attitudes he shows will link, in however inchoate a way, the questioning behaviour and the hostile attitudes in my mind. A short stretch of imagination reveals how such links can congeal a set of thoughts and coping strategies into place which are so positioned in one's mental economy that they crush the 'spring growth' (Janet Frame) of a youthful mind. Openness to the lessons of experience and the perspectives of others can easily be stunted by the premature fixing of set modes of responding and personality structures. This will tend to happen where the developing thinker is insecure or anxious because of the way that others have reacted to him. These reactions and the attitudes they convey act as the crystallizing influence which creates a psychological constitution on the basis of one's own natural tendencies.

Lest we become too gloomy and psycho-dynamically deterministic about this process we ought to help ourselves to Neurath's picture of a boat being rebuilt as it stays afloat. (He intended it as a picture of epistemology, but there is no reason why personality theory should not make use of features of mental life that have been limned in more traditional philosophical attempts to study the mind.) The obvious application to character and personality is that even if aspects of oneself are pathological (with respect to healthy or balanced interpersonal relationships) one can, as a result of experience, reform and modify them bit by bit. Our attitudes, as we shall see, can be and are modified by reflection inspired by the modelling and responses of others. The attitudes and *hexes* congealing to form a personality are built from what philosophers call propositional attitudes - beliefs, desires, expectations, intentions, and so forth - which are themselves being formed in ways that confer interesting properties upon them.

II. Normative influences, social context and mental life

Mental self-aspirations have distinctive normative properties by contrast with other facts about oneself and other persons.

> I may infer from signs and behavioural indications what my past beliefs were - "I must have believed him" - as I may infer the present beliefs of another. But one cannot infer what one's beliefs are to be, starting from now. Either one already knows, or one has to answer a normative question, to form a belief on the evidences of truth, as one takes them to be. ...
> Similarly with the two-faced concept of desire: While I make up my mind what I now want, there are no knowable facts to be expressed in the words "I want to do so-and-so". If I infer that I must already want so-and-so or that I must already have such-and-such an unconscious desire, it is still an open question whether I dissociate myself from this desire, now brought to consciousness ... do I want to get rid of this desire, if I can, or do I now endorse it? Does it now persist as a conscious desire? ... In this uncertainty there is room for deliberation, that is, for determining what is to be true for me.[10]

An uncertainty about what I think or want is not settled by further gathering of facts about my present state but by determining this or that in accordance with what I think it right to believe or desire. These normative features of mental ascriptions imply that a subject evaluates her propositional attitudes in the light of what is warranted or 'right'. The sources of such evaluations illuminate both personality development and psychiatric disorder.

One of the most fundamental things about a thinker is that she does or can reflect upon and evaluate her own thoughts and judgments. For instance, if she sees a black object on the mat, she can think <cat>[11] but, potentially at least, can then ask <Is that really a cat?>. In learning such concepts, we learn not only to respond thus and so but also to obey prescriptive norms governing our response (e.g. !call red things 'red'!). Of course, we cannot over-intellectualize this aspect of thought because it would be wrong to believe that the subject always consciously asks such questions. And the important point here is that standards governing which judgements are warranted or what one *ought* to think in a given situation underpin all of our thinking.

This basic feature of thought assumes a higher profile when one has a doubt and asks 'Ought I to believe that?'. In this case there is a formed propositional attitude, a belief, in question (e.g. <that cat is black>) rather than merely the application of a concept such as <cat> to some item or other in experience. But how are these norms, which govern our ways of thinking rather than merely describing them, imparted to a thinker? Clearly, they are imparted through the myriad reactions of others to the responses of the thinker e.g. 'That isn't a cat, silly; that's a cushion'. What is more, these reactions are continuous with the reactive attitudes that figure so prominently in the development of interpersonal relations.

At this point we can move into material more overtly relevant to psychiatry by examining a suggested distinction between presentations and representations.[12] The former are tendencies to react as if things were thus and so but they do not achieve full status as propositional attitudes e.g. the sub-conscious idea <mummy is jealous of me>. Such phenomena contrast with representations (such as the fully-fledged belief that mummy is jealous of me) which are states subject to evaluative scrutiny. We evaluate our beliefs (or doxastic states) by making judgments about their epistemic warrants. These differences in the epistemic credentials of the two types of phenomena imply that the latter states *have*, whereas the former *have not*, been engaged with reflective faculties which exercise the normative effect that Hampshire has discussed. I have already noted that the inherent norms which influence one's adoption of mental content in general and therefore of propositional attitudes in particular arise, in part, from the reactive attitudes of others toward one's past avowals and attempts at a coherent mental economy. Thus there is a close connection between usable, integrated mental content and the relationships in which one has participated. I believe that this connection can be one of the most powerful tools working on the side of the therapist who is attempting to assist a disturbed patient.

The effect of interpersonal contact is clearly seen in the treatment of *bulimia nervosa*, an eating disorder related to *anorexia nervosa* in which the patients have binges of overeating and vomiting: 'bulimia tends to start in women in late adolescence or early adulthood'; there is a 'high prevalence of depressive symptoms ... attempted suicide ... self multilating behaviour, alcohol and drug abuse, and low self esteem'.[13] A recent study compared treatment with behaviour therapy, cognitive-behaviour therapy, and group therapy and found that the respective weekly 'binge-rates' (evidently a reliable method of estimating resolution of the condition) was lowest at a year's follow up for those with group therapy.

> We conclude that *bulimia nervosa* is amenable to treatment by structured once weekly psychotherapy in either individual or group form .... provided that such patients complete the course, roughly three quarters will be symptom free at the end of 15 weeks.[14]

A further study has shown clearly that 'interpersonal therapy' is superior to both behavioural and cognitive therapy, both in terms of objective attitudes and in terms of self-esteem and relationships.[15] These findings suggest that in this disorder the reflective control of maladaptive and unconsciously driven behaviour associated with disruptions of self esteem and personal relationships is best achieved by interpersonal contact and participation in situations where reactive attitudes are shared and manifest. On the present view this would be explained by the fact that such contact enables the subject to incorporate the evaluations and reactions of sympathetic others into the structure of her own propositional attitudes and to reason about and adjust her own self-reflective thoughts.

Central in the process of recovery from a mental disorder where paradigmatically presentational/subconscious influences have distorted a patient's behaviour, is the recognition of the subject as a thinker in her own right who is constructing a mental life which embodies a range of values and self-ascriptions. The process is aided when a person is treated as having a valid perspective of her own and as a suitable focus for reactive attitudes which acknowledge her integrative and determining role in her personality and action. But complications arise because it is precisely this set of attitudes that are suspended when we move into an objective mode because the person concerned is psychologically disturbed.

III. 'Loonies'

> We had no loonies in our family, although we knew of people who had been sent 'down the line', but we did not know what they looked like, only that there was a funny look in their eye and they'd attack you with a bread knife or an axe.[16]

Thus Janet Frame describes her reactions on passing Seacliff, a mental hospital, on her first journey from home to Dunedin. Like all such places it was sited well away from the milieu of normal life. The term 'loonies' demarcates the inmates of Seacliff as undeniably different from other people and indicates that their thoughts are opaque to us, lacking sense, crazy. With those whose mental life is inexplicable in this way we feel not only at sea, but also threatened: we cannot interact with them in the ways that normally affirm or reflect our own hold on sanity and solidity. Therefore such people are marginalized, relegated to an alien status in which their thoughts do not call forth our normal reactions but rather evoke quite different behaviour.

(i) *The patient's opinions are negated or devalued.*

> No one thought to ask me why I had screamed at my mother, no one asked me what my plans were for the future. I became an instant third person, or even personless ... I was taken (third person people are thrust into the passive mood) to Seacliff.[17]

(ii) *Because the patient is reacted to as an individual who does not warrant openness, the therapeutic relationship can slide into a duplicity in which both therapist and patient manipulate each other according to their own 'hidden agendas'.*

> My consolation was my talks with [J.F.], as he was my link with the world I had known, and because I wanted these talks to continue, I built up a formidable schizophrenic repertoire: I'd lie on the couch, while the handsome [J.F.] glistening with newly applied Freud, took note of what I said and did, and suddenly I'd put a glazed look in my eye and begin to relate a fantasy as if I experienced it as a reality.[18]

There is, indeed, a fine line between acting as if you are mad and being mad, but it is almost certainly not as simple as one of my medical school teachers suggested when he said 'If you're mad enough to act mad you are mad'.

(iii) *The patient is condescended to, treated as a proprietary item or 'fey' child rather than a locus of thoughts and attitudes.*

> My shyness and self-consciousness, arising from my feelings of being nowhere, increased when my sister's friends asked, "How is she"? "Does she like being in Auckland?" I had become a third person, at home in Willowglen and now here in Auckland.[19]

(iv) *A range of barbaric and unproven treatments have been applied to psychiatric patients, allegedly in their own best interests, all of which hold terrors for any normal person.*

> I was discharged from hospital on probation. After having received over two hundred applications of unmodified E.C.T., each equivalent, in degree of fear, to an execution, and in the process having my memory shredded, and after having been subjected to proposals to have myself changed, by a physical operation, into a more acceptable, amenable, normal person, I arrived home at Willowglen, outwardly smiling and calm, but inwardly with all confidence gone, with the conviction at last that I was officially a non-person.[20]

It was later concluded that 'there had been an awful mistake even in my first admission to hospital and from then on a continued misinterpretation of my plight'.[21]

Once started, the process of being discounted as a person is hard to stop. This results in deprivation of the interpersonal contact essential to restructuring of mind and attitudes; the patient loses the normal active control over his own experience which is intrinsic to formulating a longitudinal perspective on his life as a purposeful, integrated being. He thus loses the sense of 'I' as the focus of the communications and intentions of others. All these losses perpetuate the objective, dehumanizing process and leech meaning from an already threatened individual for whom the reconstruction of meaning and identity are of central concern.

Before I proceed and you conclude that I have an entirely sociodynamic/cognitive view of mental disorder I had better offer one or two qualifying remarks. First, the disorder in a psychologically disturbed person's life is mental - it has to do with his thoughts and attitudes. Therefore the damage to be repaired is at least twofold: (i) we must remove or offset the ongoing cause of mental disarray whether that be biochemical or social/cognitive; and (ii) we must help the afflicted person reconstruct an integrated mental life where that is possible. My contention is that even where the cause of a mental disorder is clearly biological, neglect of the latter need can perpetuate the damage. A saving factor in the face of our unsystematic approach to such reconstructive work is that we have a strong tendency to relate to other human beings in terms of reactive and interpersonal attitudes and thus everyday human contact has a normalizing and therapeutic influence. That is not to say that any contact is helpful, since certain kinds of contact may well be harmful, or even, arguably, genetic in its effect on psychological problems. It is merely to say that some ongoing personal contact is essential to the reconstruction of personality and personal identity.

IV. Having an identity

Although we might not go as far as to adopt Jung's view that for human beings 'optimum development tends toward a goal called "wholeness" or "integration": a condition in which the different elements of the psyche, both conscious and unconscious, are welded together indissolubly',[22] we can recognise the central importance of being somebody, having an identity as a significant individual. I have suggested that this feature of human life is defined and refined in the ongoing interactions where one forms self-reactive attitudes and realizes certain attributes as constituting <self>.

Jean-Paul Sartre argues that the project of self-actualization is the essential defining characteristic of human consciousness. He claims that by acting in the world one becomes something and defines oneself as distinct from the context in which those actions occur. We need not, however, cast our net as far as the continental tradition to realise the crucial role of the thinker as agent and initiator in cognition and healthy human life in general.[23] This is almost the exact antipathy of what is found in many psychiatric settings.

> I grew to know and like my fellow patients. I was impressed and saddened by their - our - capacity to learn and adhere to and often relish the spoken and unspoken rules of institutional life, by the pride in the daily routine, shown by patients who had been in hospital for many

years. There was a personal, geographical, even linguistic exclusiveness in this community of the insane, who had no legal or personal external identity - no clothes of their own to wear, no handbags, purses, no possessions but a temporary bed to sleep in with a locker beside it, and a room to sit in and stare called the dayroom.[24]

The same dehumanizing lack is revealed in Solzhenitsyn's *A day in the life of Ivan Denisovich*. This aimlessness and a loss of anything which might give a sense of identity or purpose for living becomes the pattern of life for many people who suffer psychological problems. An uninspiring mental life and the discounting of self as agent can therefore undermine the endeavour to restore the patient to function as a person in his or her own right. A setting in which objective attitudes are dominant endorses this sense of inertia or passivity. Reactive attitudes, on the other hand, essentially derive from the view that the other is a locus of mental life with her own attitudes - beliefs, intentions and emotional stances. Attitudes guided by a view of the patient as a person emphasize the fact that the other is a locus of initiative and not merely a focus of states of affairs which tend to (causally) produce certain outcomes in terms of her behaviour. Seeing oneself in the light of the reactive attitudes of others is therefore a *sine qua non* of the formation of an identity and therefore of reintegration into society as a significant individual. What is more, this need not threaten a biological understanding of certain psychiatric disorders.

V. Biochemistry and mental disorder

There are certain conditions whose genesis and phenomenology rest so heavily on a biological mechanism that to deny it would just be foolish. These include at least acute schizophrenia and manic depressive psychosis and probably also depression and certain agitated mood disorders. But the system in which the biological changes act is designed to interact with and be changed by its environment as a result of experience. The system comprises a set of biochemically mediated structural-functional complexes in what is primarily a 'wet-wired' processing network. The efficient causes of change include both biochemical agents that affect transmission between units in the system and information-preserving changes in the connections of the system. The former causes entail that a model of the system which preserves only its electro-mechanical features does not accurately reflect the way that it may act and the latter means that an account of neural function in terms of humeral and pharmacological factors is also incomplete. Of these two types of influences the experimental one is of greatest interest in the present context. I have argued in a series of papers on the subject that the human organism is exquisitely sensitive to the way that items in the environment are presented to it by conspecifics.[25] The cognitive 'location' of information received and the cognitive-conative effects that it will have are determined not only by its physical/causal characteristics but also by the way it was figured in the behaviour of other human beings.

The responses of other human beings pick out items and features of the environment to which a developing thinker can then respond in such a way as to incorporate those items into his behavioural repertoire. Consider, for instance, a stone lying on the ground which may be irrelevant to a number of human thinkers until one of them picks it up and uses it as an instrument in some activity. This action constitutes the item as a thing worth noting rather than merely part of the background and sets the stage for items like it to be noted and used in future. The changes in the brain as a result of such experiences are what give rise to our cumulative abilities to adapt to the many contingencies and possibilities of situations that are captured by our language and form part of human forms of life. We would therefore expect to find something corresponding to a representation of a stone in the brain of the thinkers concerned - a node or focus of processing activity which had an explanatory role in future behaviour.[26] Notice that what is represented in the brain is an item as illuminated by human responses toward it (even the label 'stone' that we attach to such a thing is, of course, such a response). The responses concerned are manifest in practices in which human beings repeatedly or customarily react thus and so to things about them. When words are involved, the practices are shared (and thus link the responses of one person to those of others in normative ways). Where such practices focus on interpersonal exchanges and our reactions to one another, they touch chords that have been strung early in our development as thinkers and feelers. Many of our basic reactions in these areas are formed in close, indeed intense, relationships where personal needs have been recognized and met by those who care for us. Thus words and propositional attitudes involving mental ascriptions and self-ascriptions such as <he/I is/am in distress> introduce content which has been formed in close relationships in one's personal history into a current situation.

Human beings are not only active perceivers but also holistic systems in which there is a constant interplay between conative and cognitive aspects of situations. Thus thoughts and attitudes reverberate in a brain network that realizes the accumulated weight of experience in its representations of both factual and motivationally weighted states of affairs. Because the brain is best seen as an interconnected network of neuronal activity, the trains of activity that evolve in this system do not merely occur in step by step chains of causal state transitions but also in patterns of excitation that link the markers of one's mental economy into an integrated, ramified and complex whole which may often surprise us by the experiential links that are revealed and tends to escape purely rational analysis.[27] A human mind constantly links new stimuli to old in ways which open as many possibilities as they close. Because humans depend greatly on shared practices in their adaptations to their environment, the organization of the structure into which the units of such a system dispose themselves is heavily influenced by language and thus by the milieu in which linguistic expressions derive meaning from their uses.[28] This milieu is, of course, an interpersonal one in the normal case, a fact which allows a synthesis of biological and cognitive/dynamic approaches to abnormal human behaviour.

VI. Implications for psychiatry

The brain is a physiological information processor. As such it is sensitive to biochemical disruptions and therefore to those disorders which affect mental function by altering the conditions necessary for information transmission. These dysfunctions must be treated in their own terms. In the severely disordered phases of conditions like manic-depressive psychosis or acute schizophrenia, the patient's cognitive dynamics seem to resemble an electronic system which is buzzing with interfering affects so that the content that is manifest is fragmented, uncoordinated with ongoing activity and at odds with normal responses to situations. The most obvious response is to minimize or reduce the biological disruption that is confounding cognitive processes. I have suggested that the afflicted patient would seem to need two things in such crises:

(i) corrective pharmacological control to offset as far as possible the biochemical turmoil that is wreaking havoc in thought and personality function;

and

(ii) help in the reorganization of thoughts and attitudes so that mental economy can be restored and personality reconstructed. Therefore psychiatry must take an inclusive stance so as to understand the three-way interaction between biology, cognition and interpersonal activity. Such a stance allows us to act at any of the points where a person - as a rational, social and biological being - is vulnerable. The effects on the human mind of which we must take account therefore include inborn processing biases which may well lie at the root of many affective, personality and neurotic disorders, those chemical aberrations that probably give rise to the major psychoses, and the social and personal factors that can influence any psychopathology and may be the principal cause of certain types of disorder.

Social and personal factors, through their effect on the perceived contingencies of the environment, can distort the normal process of personality formation under the influence of reactive attitudes and produce a mental disorder which may be as resistant to change as any other type of dysfunction. When we recall that brain processing networks realize the cumulative effects of experience, this should not be surprising. Personal interactions literally influence the physiological 'shape' of brain function. Thus disorders arising from such processes have effects on brain function just as real as and perhaps even more enduring than any biological influence. The extent to which such effects are amenable to change would depend, in Janet Frame's terms, on the weight of 'future years' which had accumulated upon them and fixed them in place. Where such effects are of paramount importance in the genesis of a mental disorder we would expect interpersonal therapy of some type to hold the greatest hope for correction. But whatever the cause of aberrant ways of responding to the environment one would expect that rehabilitation and the acquisition of new ways of dealing with challenges would ultimately depend upon interactions in which the patient found supportive and normalizing reactive attitudes.[29] Such interpersonal contacts would play a vital role in the reconstruction of mental life and identity wherever the individual had lost his or her 'attunement' to their normal context of living.[30]

VII. Psychotherapy

Psychotherapy (in the broad sense of a cognitive dynamic approach to psychological disorders) uses techniques in which reactive and objective attitudes cannot easily be separated and is therefore distinct from other health interventions. A simple surgeon such as myself can separate the attitudes concerned quite easily: I relate to the patient as a person through discourse and cut them up as objects in an operating theatre with quite different tools and techniques. A psychotherapist has no such clear separation in much of what she does. She uses discourse both to correct the deficiencies of thought and action of which she becomes aware and as the medium of her contact with the patient as a person. (In fact, although it never ceases to puzzle me why it should be so, I am well aware that my words as much as my use of cold steel have a vital place in the recovery of my patients.) In both reactive and instrumental uses of discourse a therapist is aiming at the flourishing of the patient as a person - a rational, social being. I have stressed that to foster that aim the patient must be treated as a source of attitudes and initiatives and as having his own valid perspective on life events. But this stance often cannot be assumed from the start in the treatment of mental disorder because there is something profoundly wrong with the patient's function as a rational, social being. These facts have clear implications for right conduct in psychiatric treatment and therefore for what we might narrowly call the ethics of psychiatry.

The fact that our aim is to restore the proper functioning of a person as a focus of reactive attitudes suggests that our objective attitudes must always be recognized for what they are and regarded as a provisional and temporary stance. The patient must therefore be treated as far as is possible as a thinking being who should be encouraged to assume responsibility where he is able. This orientation was something that Janet Frame found particularly reassuring when she came to London. In the context of such an orientation the sense of self that is threatened or damaged by a psychological disorder can be revived and nurtured back into health. Thus we would expect our decisions about psychiatric patients to move from a phase of care in which the patient is disempowered because of her mental disorder (and therefore a benign paternalism in cooperation with other care-givers is appropriate), to a phase of increasing resumption of self-determination by the patient in partnership with the therapist, until the kind of autonomy characteristic of normal people (which is not nearly as great as some ethicists seem to suggest) has been restored. The return to a full panoply of truth-telling, informed consent, and confidentiality as principles operative in medical transactions goes in step with the patient's return to a personality and thought pattern which grounds reactive attitudes.

In the psychiatric patient the inability to make well-grounded choices in her own best interest is writ large and it should serve to alert us to the fact that many people have inchoate and often poorly formulated life-goals and value structures in which they seek guidance as much as freedom of choice.

That this is a general characteristic of human thinking is not often realized; that it makes a demand on doctors and health care workers as persons and not as objective observers and manipulators is realized even less often. Our patients do look to us as authority figures because of our expertise but they look for respect, guidance and care as well as management. There is a fine line between the two and we must somehow manage the patient so as to help him overcome his problems while retaining our respect for the patient as a person as the 'lodestone' for our dealings with them.

Psychiatric disorders force us to confront the tension in our attitudes to one another more clearly than many areas of human life. They also highlight the regulative ideal of all human interactions in which reactive attitudes bring us into contact with each other as *loci* of self-conscious thoughts and considered actions. Only by so doing can we register and respect each other's hopes, fears, insights, needs and intentions and so enter the participant roles that are the norm of interpersonal discourse in intelligent communities. Janet Frame descended into the 'land of shades' where she was viewed as less than a person and her thoughts devalued.

> I remember one instance of a letter written to my sister June where I was actually quoting from Virginia Woolf, in describing the gorse as having a "peanut buttery smell". This description was questioned by the doctor who read the letters, and judged to be an example of my "schizophrenia", although I had had no conversation with the doctors, or tests. I had woven myself into a trap, remembering that a trap is also a refuge.[31]

It is as well, for the sake of the world of letters and for Janet Frame as a person, that she was reinstated from her trap/refuge to the world of normal people and allowed to become one of the foremost female writers that New Zealand has ever produced.

> I joined the new town library and discovered William Faulkner and Franz Kafka, and I rediscovered the few books left on my own

bookshelf. I began to write stories and poems and to think of a future without being overcome by fear that I would be seized and "treated" without being able to escape.[32]

Notes

1. Frame, (1989) p. 149.
2. Frame, *op.cit.*, p. 222
3. Strawson, (1974), p. 6.
4. Strawson, *op.cit.*, p. 9.
5. Strawson, *op.cit.*, p. 12.
6. Jaspers, (1974), p. 84.
7. Jaspers, *op.cit.*, pp. 83f.
8. These general principles underlie Donald Davidson's view of mental states and the constraints on semantic theory but are available on a wider set of grounds.
9. Strawson, op cit., pp. 16f.
10. Hampshire, (1969), p. 37.
11. I use the notation <cat> to indicate the concept rather than the linguistic term which denotes cats.
12. Church, (1987).
13. Freeman, Barry, Dunkeld-Turnbull, and Henderson, (1988).
14. Freeman, *et al.*, *op.cit.*, p. 525.
15. Fairburn, (1988).
16. Frame, *op. cit.*, p. 150.
17. Frame, *op. cit.*, p. 191.
18. Frame, *op. cit.*, p. 201.
19. Frame, *op. cit.*, p. 215.
20. Frame, *op. cit.*, p. 224.
21. Frame, *op. cit.*, p. 277.
22. Storr, (1987), p. 159.
23. I have discussed this in, for instance, my (1987a) and (1987b).
24. Frame, *op cit*, p. 193.
25. Gillett, (1987a), (1988), (1989a).
26. On the topic of representation see my (1989b).
27. I have discussed this in my (1989b),
28. This has been clearly demonstrated by Lev Vygotsky e.g. in his (1962).
29. Of course, not all reactive attitudes are supportive and affirmative of self and helpful in psychological recovery: some reasons may be positively damaging.

30. Ulrich Neisser, describing Gibson's work on perception, used the term 'attunement' to describe the relation between the organism's brain functions and the objects and features it habitually deals with in the environment.
32. Frame, *op. cit.*, p. 213.
32. Frame, *op. cit.*, p. 225.

Bibliography

Aaron H.J. and Schwartz W.B. (1984): *The Painful Prescription: Rationing Hospital Care,* Washington D.C., The Brookings Institution.
Amundsen D.W. (1987): 'Medicine and the birth of defective children: approaches of the ancient world', in McMillan R.C. *et al* (1987) pp. 3-22.
Angell M. (1985): 'Cost containment and the physician', *Journal of the American Medical Association,* pp. 1203-07.
Anscombe G.E. (1957): *Intention,* Oxford, Basil Blackwell.
Bayles M. (1976): 'Harm to the unconceived', *Philosophy and Public Affairs,* 5, pp. 292-304.
Beller F. and Reeve J. (1989): 'Brain life and brain death: the anencephalic as an explanatory example. A contribution to transplantation', *The Journal of Medicine and Philosophy,* 14, pp. 5-23.
Binkin N. *et al.* (1984): 'Preventing neonatal herpes', *Journal of the American Medical Association,* Vol 251, pp. 2816-21.
BMA Working Party (1988): 'Conclusions of the BMA Working Party set up to review the association's guidance on euthanasia', *British Medical Journal,* 296, pp. 1376-1377.

Brandt R.B. (1974): 'The morality of abortion', in Perkins R.L. (ed), *Abortion: Pro and Con*, Cambridge (Mass.), Schenkman Publishing Co.

Brody B.A. (1983): 'Redistribution without egalitarianism', *Social Philosophy and Policy*, 1, pp. 71-87.

Brody B.A. *et al* (1991): 'The impact of economic considerations on clinical decision making', *Medical Care*, September.

Brody B.A. and Lie R. (forthcoming): 'Methodological and conceptual issues in health care system comparisons: Canada, Norway and the United States'.

Bromham D., Dalton M.G. and Jackson J.C. (eds) (1990): *Philosophical Ethics in Reproductive Medicine*, Manchester, Manchester University Press.

Buckle S. *et al.* (eds) (1990): *Embryo Experimentation*, Cambridge, Cambridge University Press.

Budin P. (1907): *The Nursling: the Feeding and Hygiene of Premature and Full-Term Infants*, London, The Caxton Publishing Co.

Butler S.M. (1991): 'A tax reform strategy to deal with the uninsured', *Journal of the American Medical Association*, vol 265, pp. 2541-44.

Callahan D. (1970): *Abortion: Law, Choice and Morality*, London, Macmillan.

Callahan J.C. (1987): 'On harming the dead', *Ethics*, 97, pp. 341-352.

Campbell A.G.M. (1982): 'Which infants should not receive intensive care?', *Archives of Disease in Childhood*, 57, pp. 569-571.

Campbell A.G.M., Duff R. (1979): Authors' response to Richard Sherlock's commentary: selective treatment of newborns, *Journal of Medical Ethics*, 5, pp. 141-2.

Capron A.M. (1987): 'Anencephalic donors: separate the dead from the dying', *Hastings Center Report*, 17, 1, pp. 5-8.

Chasnoff *et al.* (1989): 'Temporal patterns of cocaine use in pregnancy: perinatal outcome', *Journal of American Medical Association*, 261, 12, p.1741.

Church J. (1987): 'Reasonable irrationality' *Mind*, XCVI, pp. 354-66.

Churchill, D.N., Morgan J. and Torrance G.W. (1984): 'Quality of life in end-stage renal disease', *Peritoneal Dialysis Bulletin* 4, pp 20-23.

Commentary (1884): *Lancet*, i, p.266.
Daniels N. (1985): *Just Health Care*, Cambridge, Cambridge University Press, 1985.
Daniels N. (1986): 'Why saying no to patients in the United States is so hard', *New England Journal of Medicine*, vol. 314, pp. 1380-83.
Dawson N.V. *et al.* (1990): 'Phase II: influencing decision making in SUPPORT', *Journal of Clinical Epidemiology*, vol. 43 Suppl, pp 103S-108S.
Depp, Sabbagha, Brown, Tamura and Reedy (1983): 'Fetal surgery for hydrocephalus: successful *in utero* ventriculoamniotic shunt for Dandy-Walker syndrome', 61 *Obstetrics and Gynecology* 710.
Devlin Lord P. (1959): 'The enforcement of morals', *Proceedings of the British Academy*, 45.
Duff R.S., Campbell A.G. (1973): 'Moral and ethical dilemmas in the special care nursery', *New England Journal of Medicine*, 289, pp. 890-94.
Duff R.S., Campbell A.G.M. (1987): 'Moral communities and tragic choices' in McMillan R.C., Englehardt H.T. Jr, Spicker S.F. (eds), (1987), pp. 273-89.
Durey M.J. (1976): 'Bodysnatchers and Benthamites: the implications of the Dead Body Bill for the London Schools of Anatomy, 1820-42', *London Journal*, 2, 2, pp. 200-25.
Dworkin R. (1989): 'The great abortion case', *New York Review of Books*, 36, nr. 11, pp. 49-53.
Elias S. and Annas G. (1987): *Reproductive Genetics and the Law*.
Ellison P.H. (1984): 'Neurologic development of the high-risk infant', *Clinics in Perinatology*, 11, (1), pp. 41-58.
Ellison P., Horn J., Browning C. (1983): 'A large sample, many variable study of motor dysfunction of infancy', *Journal of Pediatric Psychiatry*, 8, pp. 345-57.
Enthoven A. and Kronick R. (1989): 'A consumer-choice health plan for the 1990s', *New England Journal of Medicine*, vol. 320, pp. 29-37, 94-101.
Ethics and Social Impact Committee of the Transplant Policy Center, Ann Arbour, Michigan (1988): 'Anencephalic infants as sources of transplantable organs', *Hastings Center Report*, 18, 5, pp. 28-30.
Evans R.W. *et al* (1985): 'The quality of life of patients with end-stage renal disease', *New England Journal of Medicine*, 312, 9, pp. 553-59.

Fairburn C. (1988): 'Current status of the psychological treatment for *bulimia nervosa'*, *Journal of Psychosomatic Research*, 32, 6, pp. 635-645.
Feinberg J. (1984): *Harm to Others: the Moral Limits of the Criminal Law*, Oxford, Oxford University Press.
Feinberg J. (1985): 'The mistreatment of dead bodies', *Hastings Center Report*, 15, 1, pp. 31-37.
Fleischman A.R. (1986): 'An infant bioethical review committee in an urban medical center', *Hastings Center Report*, 16, 3, pp.16-18.
Foot P. (1981): 'The problem of abortion and the doctrine of the double effect', in Foot P, *Virtues and Vices and other essays in moral philosophy*, Berkeley, University of California Press.
Ford N. (1989): *When Did I Begin?*, Cambridge, Cambridge University Press.
Frame J. (1989): *An Autobiography*, Auckland (NZ), Century Hutchinson.
Freeman C.P.L., Barry F., Dunkeld-Turnbull J., Henderson A. (1988): 'Controlled trial of psychotherapy for *bulimia nervosa'*, *British Medical Journal*, 296, pp. 521-525.
Fries J.F. (1980): 'Aging, natural death, and the compression of morbidity', *New England Journal of Medicine*, vol. 303, pp. 130-36
Frohock F.M. (1986): *Special Care*, Chicago, University of Chicago Press.
Gaitz C.M. *et al* (1985): *Aging 2000, Vol. II*, New York, Springer Verlag.
Gallagher J. (1987): 'Prenatal invasions and interventions: what's wrong with fetal rights', 10 *Harvard Women's Law Journal* 9.
Gaylin W. (1974): 'Harvesting the dead', *Harper's Magazine*, Sept., pp. 23-46.
Gillett G. (1987a): 'The generality constraint and conscious thought'. *Analysis*, 47, 1, pp. 20-24.
Gillett G. (1987b): 'Reasoning about persons', in Peacocke and Gillett (eds) (1987), pp. 75-88.
Gillett G. (1988): 'Learning to perceive', *Philosophy and Phenomenological Research*, XLVIII, 4, pp. 601-18.
Gillett G. (1989a): 'Perception and neuroscience', *British Journal for the Philosophy of Science*, 40, 1, pp. 83-103.
Gillett G. (1989b): 'Representations and cognitive science', *Inquiry*, 32, pp. 262-76.

Glover J. (1977): *Causing Death and Saving Lives*, Harmondsworth, Penguin Books.
Glover J. *et al.* (1989); *Fertility and the Family: The Glover Report on Reproductive Technologies to the European Commission*, London, Fourth Estate Ltd.
Goldberg (1989): 'Medical choices during pregnancy: whose decision is it anyway?', 42 *Rutgers Law Review* 591.
Gordon R.M. (1976): 'The abortion issue', in Freeman E (ed), *The Abdication of Philosophy: Philosophy and the Public Good*, La Salle, Ill., Open Court.
Green M.B. and Wikler D. (1980): 'Brain death and personal identity', *Philosophy and Public Affairs*, 9, 2, pp. 105-33.
Grene M. (1968): *Approaches to a Philosophical Biology*, New York, Basic Books.
Grobstein C. (1988): *Science and the Unborn*, New York, Basic Books.
Gudex C. (1986): 'QALYs and their use by the Health Service', York, England: University of York, Centre for Health Economics, Discussion Paper 20.
Hampshire S. (1969): 'Some difficulties in knowing', in Morgenbesser, Suppes and White (eds), *Philosophy, Science and Method*, London, Macmillan.
Hare R.M. (1975): 'Abortion and the golden rule', *Philosophy and Public Affairs*, 4, pp. 201-22.
Harris J. (1985): *The Value of Life*, London, Routledge and Kegan Paul.
Harris J. (1986a): 'Rationing life: quality or justice', Address to British Medical Association Annual Scientific Meeting, Oxford, 12 April, 1986.
Harris J. (1986b): 'QALYfying the value of life' (revised version of address to British Medical Association Annual Scientific Meeting, Oxford, April 1986), University of Manchester, Department of Education.
Harrison *et al.* (1982): 'Fetal surgery for congenital hydronephrosis', *New England Journal of Medicine*, 306, p. 591.
Harrison M.R. (1986): 'The anencephalic newborn as organ donor', *Hastings Center Report* , 16, 2, pp. 21-22.
Hart H.L.A. and Honore A.M. (1959), *Causation in the Law*, London, Oxford University Press.
Hayry M. and Hayry H. (1987): *Rakasta karsi ja unhoita: Moraalfilosofisia pohdintojaihmiselaman alusta ja lopusta (Moral philosophical reflections*

on the beginning and end of life) (in Finnish), Helsinki, Kirjayhtyma.
Hayry M and Hayry H (1989): 'Ihmisokeudet, moraali ja lisaatymisen vapaus' ('Human rights, morals and reproductive freedom', in Finnish), in Hayry H. and Hayry M.(eds), *Luonnotonta lastensaantia? (Unnatural Children?)*, Helsinki, Gaudeamus.
Holbrook D. (1985): 'Medical ethics and the potentialities of the living being', *British Medical Journal*, 291, pp. 459-62.
Hubbell F.A. *et al* (1985): 'The impact of routine admission chest X-ray films on patient care', *New England Journal of Medicine*, vol. 312, pp. 209-13.
Hume D. (1978): *A Treatise of Human Nature*, Oxford, Clarendon Press, 2nd edn.
Jaspers K. (1974): 'Causal and meaningful connexions between life history and psychosis', in Hirsch S.R. and Shepherd M. (eds), *Themes and Variations in European Psychiatry,* Bristol, John Wright.
Jonas H. (1974): 'Against the stream: comments on the definition and redefinition of death', in his *Philosophical Essays*, Englewood Cliffs, N.J., Prentice-Hall.
Jones-Lee M.W. (ed). (1982): *The Value of Life and Society,* Amsterdam, Elsevier/North Holland.
Kaplan R.M. and Bush J.W. (1982): 'Health-related quality of life measurement for evaluation research and policy analysis', *Health Psychology,* 1, 1, pp. 61-80
Kennedy I.M. (1981): *The Unmasking of Medicine,* Hemel Hempstead, Allen and Unwin.
Kennedy I.M. (1988): *Treat Me Right: Essays in Medical Law and Ethics*, Oxford, Clarendon Press.
Kenny A. (1978): *Freewill and Responsibility,* London, Routledge and Kegan Paul.
Kind P.; Rosser R.; and Williams A. (1982): 'Valuation of quality of life: some psychometric evidence', in Jones-Lee (ed.) (1982), pp. 159-70.
Kuhse H. (1984): 'A modern myth: that letting die is not the intentional causation of death: some reflections on the trial and acquittal of Dr. Leonard Arthur', *Journal of Applied Philosophy,*1, 1, pp. 21-38.
Kuhse H. (1987): *The Sanctity of Life Doctrine in Medicine*, Oxford, Clarendon Press.
Kuhse H. and Singer P. (1985): *Should the Baby Live? The Problem of Handicapped Infants*, Oxford, Oxford University Press.

Kuhse H. and Singer P. (1989): 'From the editors', *Bioethics* 3, pp. iii-vi.
Kuhse H. and Singer P. (1990): 'Individuals, humans and persons: the issue of moral status', in Buckle S *et al* (eds) (1990), pp. 65-75.
Lamb D. (1985): *Death, Brain Death and Ethics*, London, Croom Helm.
Lamb D. (1990): *Ethics and Organ Transplants*, London, Routledge.
Law S.A. (1984): 'Rethinking sex and the constitution', *University of Pennsylvania Law Review*, 132, p. 955.
Lees D. and Shaw S. (eds) (1974): *Impairment, Disability and Handicap*, London, Heinemann for the Social Sciences Research Council.
Lemire R.J., Beckwith J.B. and Warkang J. (1978): *Anencephaly*, New York, Raven Press.
Lenow J. (1983): 'The fetus as a patient: emerging rights as a person?', 9 *American Journal of Law and Medicine* 1.
Levenbrook B.B. (1984): 'Harming someone after his death', *Ethics* 1984, pp. 407-49.
Lockwood M. (1985a): 'When does life begin?', in Lockwood M. (ed.), *Moral Dilemmas in Modern Medicine*, Oxford, Oxford University Press, pp. 9-31.
Lockwood M. (1985b): 'The Warnock Report: a philosophical appraisal', in Lockwood M. (ed), *Moral Dilemmas in Modern Medicine*, Oxford, Oxford University Press, pp. 155-86.
Lockwood M. (1988): 'Warnock versus Powell (and Harradine): when does potentiality count?', *Bioethics* II, 3, pp. 187-213.
Lowe (1980): 'Wardship and abortion prevention - further observations', 96 *Law Quarterly Review* 29.
Lyon J. (1985): *Playing God in the Nursery*, New York and London, W.W. Norton and Co.
McCormick R.A. (1974): 'To save or let die: the dilemma of modern medicine', *Journal of the American Medical Association*, 229, 2, pp. 172-76.
McMillan R. *et al* (eds) (1987): *Euthanasia and the Newborn*, Dordrecht, Reidel.
Mason J.K. (1988): *Human Life and Medical Practice*, Edinburgh, Edinburgh University Press.
May W. (1972): 'Attitudes towards the newly dead', *The Hastings Center Studies* I, pp. 3-13.
Maynard A. (1986): Address to the British Medical Association Annual Scientific Meeting, Oxford, 12 April.

Mennuti M.T. (1989): 'Prenatal diagnosis - advances bring new challenges', *New England Journal of Medicine* 320, 10, p.661-63.
Menzel P.T. (1990): *Strong Medicine: the Ethical Rationing of Health Care*, New York, Oxford University Press.
Milunsky A. (1989): *Choices, Not Chances*, Boston, Little, Brown and Co.
Morgan D. (1989): 'Letting babies die legally', *Bulletin of the Institute of Medical Ethics*, 50, 5, pp.13-18.
Morison R.S. (1971): 'Death: process or event?', *Science*, 173, pp. 694-98.
Mossner E.C. (1980): *The Life of David Hume*, Second edition, Oxford, Oxford University Press.
Muller J. *et al* (1980): 'Fetal loss after implantation', *Lancet*, 2, pp. 554-56.
Murray (1987): 'Moral obligations to the not-yet born: the fetus as patient', 14 *Clinics Perinatology* 329.
Nelson, Buggy and Weil (1986): 'Forced medical treatment of pregnant women: 'Compelling each to live as seems good to the rest', 37 *Hastings Law Journal* 703.
Nelson L.J. and Milliken N. (1988): 'Compelled medical treatment of pregnant women', 259 *Journal of the American Medical Association* 1060.
Noonan J.T. Jr. (1970): 'An almost absolute value in history', in Noonan J.T. Jr. (ed), *The Morality of Abortion: Legal and Historical Perspectives*, Cambridge (Mass.), Harvard University Press.
Note (1986): 'The creation of fetal rights: conflicts with women's constitutional rights to liberty, privacy, and equal protection', 95 *Yale Law Journal*, 599, pp. 614-20.
Note (1987): 'Maternal substance abuse: the need to provide legal protection for the fetus', 60 *Southern California Law Review* 1209.
Note (1988): 'Maternal rights and fetal wrongs: the case against the criminalization of fetal abuse', 101 *Harvard Law Review* 994, pp. 955-1002 and 1009-12.
O'Donnell M. (1986): 'One man's burden', *British Medical Journal*, 293, 6538, p. 59.
Office of Technology Assessment (1980): *The Implications of Cost-Effectiveness Analysis of Medical Technology*, Washington D.C., Government Printing Office.

Office of Technology Assessment (1985): *Technology and Aging in America*, Washington D.C., Government Printing Office.
Pallis C. (1983): *The ABC of Brainstem Death*, London, British Medical Journal.
Parness (1988): 'Crimes against the unborn: protecting and respecting the potentiality of human life', 22 *Harvard Journal on Legislation*, 97, pp. 171-172.
Peacocke A.R.. and Gillett G. (eds): *Persons and Personality*, Oxford, Blackwell, 1987.
Pitcher G.(1984): 'The misfortunes of the dead', *American Philosophical Quarterly*, 21, 2, pp. 183-88.
Powell T.G., Pharoah P.O.D., Cooke R.W.I. (1986): 'Survival and morbidity in a geographically defined population of low-birthweight infants', *Lancet*, i, pp. 539-43.
President's Commission for the study of Ethical Problems in Medicine and Biomedical and Behavioural Research, The (1983): *Deciding to Forego Life-Sustaining Treatment*, Washington D.C., Government Printing Office.
Pucetti R. (1976): 'The conquest of death', *The Monist*, 59, pp. 249-63.
Pucetti R. (1988): 'Does anyone survive neocortical death?', in Zaner R. M. (ed), *Death: Beyond Whole-Brain Criteria*, Dordrecht, Kluwer Academic Publishers, pp. 75-90.
Purtilo R.B. (1984): 'Ethics consultations in the hospital', *New England Journal of Medicine*, 311, pp. 983-86.
Rachels J. (1986): *The End of Life*, Oxford, Oxford University Press.
Ramsey P. (1970): 'Points in deciding about abortion', in Noonan J.T. Jr. (ed), *The Morality of Abortion: Legal and Historical Perspectives*, Cambridge (Mass.), Harvard University Press.
Ramsey P. (1978): *Ethics at the Edges of Life: Medical and Legal Intersections*, New Haven and London, Yale University Press.
Raphael D.D. (1988): 'Handicapped infants: medicine, ethics and the law', *Journal of Medical Ethics*, 14, pp. 5-10.
Rhoden N.K. (1986a): 'Treating Baby Doe: the ethics of uncertainty', *Hastings Center Report*, 16, 4, pp. 34-42.

Rhoden N.K. (1986b): 'The judge in the delivery room: the emergence of court-ordered caesarians', 74 *California Law Review* 1951.
Roberts C and Lowe C (1975): 'Where have all the conceptions gone?', *Lancet*, 1, pp. 498-99.
Robertson J.A., Fost N. (1976): 'Passive euthanasia of defective newborn infants: legal considerations', *Journal of Pediatrics*, 88, pp. 883-89.
Robertson J.A. (1983): 'Procreative liberty and the control of conception, pregnancy and childbirth', 69 *Virginia Law Review*, 405.
Robertson J.A. (1985): 'Legal issues in fetal therapy', *Seminars in Perinatology*, Vol. 9, No. 2, p. 136.
Rosser R. and Kind P. (1978): 'A scale of valuations of states of illness: is there a social consensus?', *International Journal of Epidemiology*, 7, 4, pp. 347-58.
Rothman L.B.K. (1986): 'When a pregnant woman endangers her fetus', *Hastings Center Report*, 16, 1, p. 25.
Sass H.M. and Massey R.U. (1988): *Health Care Systems*, Dordrecht, Kluwer.
Schieber G.J. and Poullier J.P. (1989): 'International health care expenditure trends: 1987', *Health Affairs*, (Fall).
Schieber G.J. and Poullier J.P. (1991): 'International health spending: issues and trends', *Health Affairs*, (Spring).
Schwartz W. (1987): 'The inevitable failure of current cost-containment strategies', *Journal of the American Medical Association*, pp. 220-24.
Shaw M.W. (1987): 'When does treatment constitute a harm?, in McMillan R. C *et al* (eds), pp. 117-137.
Shelp E.E. (ed.) (1981): *Justice and Health Care*, Dordrecht, D. Reidel Publishing Co.
Shelp E.E. (1986): *Born to Die: Deciding the Fate of Critically Ill Newborns*, New York, Free Press.
Sher G. (1977): 'Hare, abortion and the golden rule', *Philosophy and Public Affairs*, 6, pp. 185-190.
Sherlock R. (1979): 'Selective non-treatment of newborns', *Journal of Medical Ethics*, 5, pp. 139-42.
Shewmon A.D. (1988): 'Anencephaly: selected medical aspects', *Hastings Center Report*, 18, 5, pp. 11-18.

Shewmon A.D., Capron A.M. Peacock J.W., Schulman B.L. (1989): 'The use of anencephalic infants as organ sources: a critique', *Journal of the American Medical Association*, 261, 12, pp. 1773-1781.
Silverman W.A. (1981): 'Mismatched attitudes about neonatal death', *Hastings Center Report* 11, 6, pp. 12-16.
Singer P. (1979): *Practical Ethics*, Cambridge, Cambridge University Press.
Singer P. (1989): *Animal Liberation*, 2nd edn., New York Review and Random House.
Singer P. and Dawson K. (1988): 'IVF technology and the argument from potential', *Philosophy and Public Affairs*, 17, pp. 87-104.
Spicker S *et al* (1987): *Ethical Dimensions of Geriatric Care*, Dordrecht, Kluwer.
Steinbock B. (1980): *Killing and Letting Die*, Englewood Cliffs, N.J., Prentice Hall.
Storr A. (1987): 'Jung's concept of personality', in Peacocke and Gillett (eds) (1987), pp. 150-163.
Strawson P. (1974): *Freedom and Resentment and other essays*, London, Methuen.
Teeling Smith G. (ed) (1984): *Measuring the Social Benefits of Medicine*, London, Office of Health Economics.
Teeling Smith G. (1985): *The Measurement of Health*, London, Office of Health Economics.
Thomas J. (ed.) (1983): *Medical Ethics and Human Life*, Toronto, Samuel Stevens and Company.
Thomson J.J. (1971): 'A defense of abortion', *Philosophy and Public Affairs*, 1, pp. 47-66.
Thomson J.J. (1973): 'Rights and deaths', *Philosophy and Public Affairs*, 2, pp. 146-59.
Tooley M. (1972): 'Abortion and infanticide', *Philosophy and Public Affairs*, 2, pp. 37-65.
Torrance, G.W. (1986): 'Measurement of health state utilities for economic appraisal: a review', *Journal of Health Economics*, 5, pp. 1-30.
Trounson A. (1990): 'Why do research on human embryos?', in Buckle S *et al* (eds) (1990), pp. 14-25.
Veatch R.M. (1989): *Death, Dying and the Biological Revolution: Our last Quest for Responsibility*, Revised Edition, New Haven, Yale University Press.
Vygotsky L. (1962): *Thought and Language*, transl. Hanfmann E. and Vakar G., Cambridge (Mass), MIT Press.

Wade N. (1978): 'The quick, the dead, and the cadaver population', *Science, March 31.*
Walters J.W. and Ashwal S. (1988): 'Organ prolongation in anencephalic infants: ethical and medical issues', *Hastings Center Report*, 18, 5, pp. 19-27.
Walton D.N. (1980): *Brain Death: Ethical Considerations*, West Lafayette, Indiana, Purdue University Press.
Waluchow W.J. (1986): 'Feinberg's theory of "preposthumous" harm', *Dialogue* 25, pp. 727-34.
Warnock Committee (1984): *Report of the Committee of Inquiry into Human Fertilisation and Embryology*, London, Her Majesty's Stationery Office.
Warnock M. (1985a): *A Question of Life: the Warnock Report on Human Fertilization and Embryology*, Oxford, Basil Blackwell.
Warnock M. (1985b): 'The artificial family', in Lockwood M. (ed), *Moral Dilemmas in Modern Medicine*, Oxford, Oxford University Press, pp. 138-54.
Warren M.A. (1973): 'On the moral and legal status of abortion', *The Monist*, 57, 1, pp. 43-61.
Warren M.A. (1988): 'The moral significance of birth', *Bioethics News*, 7, nr. 2.
Warren M.A. (1990): 'Is IVF research a threat to women's autonomy?', in Buckle S. *et al* (eds) (1990), pp. 125-140.
Weinstein M.C. and Stason B. (1977): 'Foundations of cost-effectiveness analysis for health and medical practices', *New England Journal of Medicine*, 296, pp. 716-21.
Weir R.F. (1984): *Selective Non-Treatment of Handicapped Newborns*, Oxford and New York, Oxford University Press.
Williams A. (1981): 'Welfare economics and health status measurement', in Perlman and van der Gaag (eds) (1981), pp. 271-81.
Williams A. (1984): 'The economic role of "health indicators"', in Teeling Smith (ed), pp. 63-67.
Williams A. (1985a): 'Economics of coronary artery bypass grafting', *British Medical Journal*, 291, pp. 326-29.
Williams A. (1985b): 'The value of QALYs', *Health and Social Service Journal*, July 18, 'Centre Eight' supplement, pp. 3-5.
Williams A. (1986a): 'Health economics: the cheerful face of the dismal science?', address to the

Annual Meeting of the British Association for the Advancement of Science, September 1-5.
Williams A. (1986b): *British Medical Journal*, 293, 6542, pp. 337-38.
Willke J.C. and Andrushko D. (1988): 'Personhood redux', *Hastings Center Report*, 18, 5, pp. 30-33.
Zuckerman *et al.* (1989): 'Effects of maternal marijuana and cocaine use on fetal growth', *New England Journal of Medicine*, 320, 12, p.762.

Index